100 MENTAL MATHS

100 MENTAL MATHS ACTIVITIES

YEAR 5

Yvette McDaniel and
Margaret Gronow

Authors
Yvette McDaniel
Margaret Gronow

Illustrations
Garry Davies

Series Designer
Sonja Bagley

Designer
Quadrum

British Library Cataloguing-in-Publication Data
A catalogue record for this book is available from the British Library.

ISBN 978-1407-11419-4

Designed using Adobe InDesign

Published by Scholastic Ltd
Book End
Range Road
Witney
Oxfordshire OX29 0YD

www.scholastic.co.uk

Printed by Bell and Bain Ltd, Glasgow

1 2 3 4 5 6 7 8 9 0 1 2 3 4 5 6 7 8 9

CONTENTS

Introduction

About the series

100 Mental Maths Activities is a series of six photocopiable teachers' resource books, one for each of Years 1–6. Each book offers a bank of mental maths activities, each designed to last between five and ten minutes. The activities are designed to fit the planning guidelines of the *Renewed Framework for Teaching Mathematics* (2007) and are therefore divided into five Blocks with three Units of work in each Block.

This series provides a valuable accompaniment to *100 Maths Framework Lessons* (Scholastic, 2007). The mental maths activities are designed to accompany lessons in the framework series and grids are provided at the start of each Block to indicate the lesson and page numbers of the associated lesson plans in the relevant *100 Maths Framework Lessons* book. Used together, the teacher will have a rich bank of resources, activities and questions, offering greater choice and variety, while keeping to a closely similar mathematical content and progression. It is for the teacher to decide when to repeat an activity and when to move on: the exact mix of consolidation and progression needed will vary from one class to another. However, the series is also wholly appropriate for independent use alongside any maths scheme of work.

The six Rs of oral and mental work

In addition to matching the content of the Renewed Framework, this series also reflects the six features of children's mathematical learning that oral and mental work can support identified by the Primary National Strategy when renewing the Framework. The 'six Rs' provide a valuable guide to the purposes of each starter and a 'type of starter' is offered alongside each of the activities in this book.

The six types of starter include:

- rehearse: practising and consolidating known skills
- recall: securing knowledge of facts – usually number facts
- refresh: drawing on, revisiting or assessing previous knowledge and skills
- refine: sharpening methods and procedures (eg mental strategies)
- read: using mathematical vocabulary and interpreting mathematical images, diagrams and vocabulary correctly
- reason: using and applying acquired knowledge and skills; using reasoning to draw conclusions.

For further information on the 'six Rs' visit the National Strategies website: *www.nationalstrategies.standards.dcsf.gov.uk.*

About the book

Each book provides support for teachers through 15 Units of mental maths, developing and practising skills that will have been introduced, explained and explored in your main maths lesson time. Few resources are needed, and the questions for each activity are provided in full. The books are complete with answers, ready for you to pick up and use.

The activities are suitable for use with single- or mixed-ability groups and single- or mixed-age classes, as much emphasis has been placed on the use of differentiated and open-ended questions. Differentiated questions ensure that all the children can be included in each lesson and have the chance to succeed; suitable questions can be directed at chosen individuals, almost guaranteeing success and thus increased confidence.

Several essential photocopiable resource pages are also included (see pages 86–95). These resources are listed alongside each activity where required and should be prepared in advance of each mental maths session.

Each activity in this book has one or more learning objective based on the Year 5 teaching programme in the Renewed Framework. Curriculum grids are presented at the start of each Block to assist teachers with their planning and to highlight links with the related *100 Maths Framework Lessons* title. Alongside the activity description, required resources are highlighted, as well as the 'type of starter' (see above for further information). Where appropriate a 'mental strategy' for solving a number sentence or problem is suggested. Discussion of the children's methods is encouraged, since this will help the children to develop mathematical language skills: to appreciate that no single method is necessarily 'correct' and that a flexible repertoire of approaches is useful; to improve their overall confidence as they come to realise that all responses have value. Strategies are encouraged that will enable the children to progress from the known to the unknown number facts, thus developing their ability to select and use methods of mental calculation.

In Year 5, emphasis is placed on learning and using multiplication facts to 10 × 10 and the related division facts. The lessons provide frequent opportunities for the development of individual strategies when manipulating numbers. Children's understanding of the inverse nature of addition/subtraction and multiplication/division is encouraged, as is their knowledge of factors, multiples and doubles. Emphasis is placed on fractions and their equivalents. Place value and decimals, rounding and the strategy of estimating and then checking are also covered. The use of all four operations to solve a variety of real-life problems involving money and measures is included. Opportunities are provided to consolidate addition and subtraction strategies developed in earlier years.

Games are included in each term's work to provide variety and generate enthusiasm for numbers. Open-ended questions are used to challenge the children and extend their thinking, while pair and group activities are used to encourage discussion and give the children opportunities to explain outcomes to the class.

Transitional assessments

Transition is a time when, historically, children dip in their performance. Why this occurs is open to discussion but schools are increasingly aware of the need to accurately track children during these periods in order to ensure, as far as possible, a smooth learning journey. Transitional assessment is therefore important not just as a tool for summative judgements at the end of a school year, but also for communicating with teaching colleagues across the school.

100 Mental Maths Activities Year 5 includes three photocopiable single-level transitional assessments for levels 4 and 5, which will provide evidence of where children have reached in relation to national standards. Printable tests, mark schemes and answer sheets are available on pages 96–111.

BLOCK A

BLOCK A

Unit 1

100 Mental Maths Starters				100 Maths Lessons		
Page	Objective	Activity title	Starter type	Unit	Lesson	Page
8	Count from any given number in whole-number and decimal steps, extending beyond zero when counting backwards; relate the numbers to their position on a number line.	(1) Clap counter	Rehearse	1	1	10
8	Explain what each digit represents in whole numbers and decimals with up to two places, and partition, round and order these numbers.	(2) Digit shuffle	Refresh	1	2	10
9	Use knowledge of place value and addition and subtraction of two-digit numbers to derive sums and differences and doubles and halves of decimals (eg 6.5 ± 2.7, half of 5.6, double 0.34).	(3) Tenths and units	Rehearse	1	4	12
9	Extend mental methods for whole-number calculations, for example to multiply a two-digit by a one-digit number (eg 12 × 9), to multiply by 25 (eg 16 × 25).	(4) Multiplication words	Recall	1	7	14
10	Use efficient written methods to add and subtract whole numbers and decimals with up to two places.	(5) Extending number bonds	Refine	1	8	15
11	Count from any given number in whole-number and decimal steps, extending beyond zero when counting backwards; relate the numbers to their position on a number line.	(6) What comes next?	Rehearse	1	10	17

Unit 2

100 Mental Maths Starters				100 Maths Lessons		
Page	Objective	Activity title	Starter type	Unit	Lesson	Page
12	Identify pairs of factors of two-digit whole numbers and find common multiples (eg for 6 and 9).	(7) What factors?	Recall	2	1	22
12	Use understanding of place value to multiply and divide whole numbers and decimals by 10, 100 or 1000.	(8) Ten times bigger	Refine	2	3	23
13	Explain reasoning using diagrams, graphs and text; refine ways of recording using images and symbols.	(9) Venn Bingo sort	Reason	2	5	25
14	Recall quickly multiplication facts up to 10 × 10 and use them to multiply pairs of multiples of 10 and 100; derive quickly corresponding division facts.	(10) Halves around the room	Recall	2	6	26

BLOCK A

Unit 2 ...continued

100 Mental Maths Starters				100 Maths Lessons		
Page	Objective	Activity title	Starter type	Unit	Lesson	Page
15	Solve one-step and two-step problems involving whole numbers and decimals and all four operations, choosing and using appropriate calculation strategies, including calculator use.	(11) Word problems Bingo	Reason	2	8	27
16	Recall quickly multiplication facts up to 10 × 10 and use them to multiply pairs of multiples of 10 and 100; derive quickly corresponding division facts.	(12) What's the question?	Recall	2	10	28

Unit 3

100 Mental Maths Starters				100 Maths Lessons		
Page	Objective	Activity title	Starter type	Unit	Lesson	Page
16	Explain what each digit represents in whole numbers and decimals with up to two places, and partition, round and order these numbers.	(13) Building numbers	Refine	3	1	36
17	Use knowledge of place value and addition and subtraction of two-digit numbers to derive sums and differences and doubles and halves of decimals (eg 6.5 ± 2.7, half of 5.6, double 0.34).	(14) Decimal pairs	Rehearse	3	4	38
17	Recall quickly multiplication facts up to 10 × 10 and use them to multiply pairs of multiples of 10 and 100; derive quickly corresponding division facts.	(15) Division Bingo	Recall	3	5	39
18	Count from any given number in whole-number and decimal steps, extending beyond zero when counting backwards; relate the numbers to their position on a number line.	(16) Order! Order!	Recall	3	8	41
19	Solve one-step and two-step problems involving whole numbers and decimals and all four operations, choosing and using appropriate calculation strategies, including calculator use.	(17) Summer-fair problems	Rehearse	3	9	42
20	Use knowledge of rounding, place value, number facts and inverse operations to estimate and check calculations.	(18) Approximations	Reason	3	10	43

1 Clap counter

Resources None	**Learning objective** Count from any given number in whole-number and decimal steps, extending beyond zero when counting backwards; relate the numbers to their position on a number line. **Type of starter** Rehearse **Mental strategy** Discuss some of the patterns that emerge.

No set answers

The class must count together from each start number in steps of a given size. They change the direction of the count each time you clap your hands.

1. from 25 in 10s
2. from 3 in 5s
3. from 50 in 25s
4. from 25 in 50s
5. from 6 in 4s
6. from 135 in 20s
7. from 13 in 3s
8. from 12 in 11s

Digit shuffle

Resources A board or flipchart; numeral cards 0-9 (from photocopiable page 89) one set per pair; place value arrow cards (from photocopiable page 88); whiteboards and pens	**Learning objective** Explain what each digit represents in whole numbers and decimals with up to two places, and partition, round and order these numbers. **Type of starter** Refresh **Mental strategy** Discuss with the children the value of each digit, using the arrow cards to demonstrate this. Ask them to explain their strategy for making the largest possible number, eg selecting the larger digits to put first, representing a higher place value, and the reverse for the smallest number. Encourage them to create all other possible numbers, either in ascending or descending order. Discuss the effect of a zero at the beginning of a number.

No set answers

Ask pairs of children to select five digits from their numeral cards.

Arrange them so that they make the largest and the smallest number possible. Ask the children to record these on their whiteboards and then to rearrange the digits to make all other possible numbers in between and record them in order. Repeat with five different digits.

This activity can be repeated using 'human' digit holders. Discuss where the digits should be placed and the human digits must move accordingly.

3 Tenths and units

Learning objective
Use knowledge of place value and addition and subtraction of two-digit numbers to derive sums and differences and doubles and halves of decimals (eg 6.5 ± 2.7, half of 5.6, double 0.34).

Type of starter
Rehearse

Resources
None

Divide the class into groups of three. Each group should work out 'how many more to 10', with the first child saying the number of tenths, the second saying the number of units and the third saying the answer (for example '9 tenths, 3 units, 3 point 9').

1. 6.1
2. 8.2
3. 4.9
4. 2.8
5. 7.7
6. 3.5
7. 1.6
8. 5.3
9. 5.6
10. 2.4
11. 5.8
12. 8.5

Answers

1. 3.9
2. 1.8
3. 5.1
4. 7.2
5. 2.3
6. 6.5
7. 8.4
8. 4.7
9. 4.4
10. 7.6
11. 4.2
12. 1.5

4 Multiplication words

Learning objective
Extend mental methods for whole-number calculations, for example to multiply a two-digit by a one-digit number (eg 12 × 9), to multiply by 25 (eg 16 × 25).

Type of starter
Recall

Resources
None

Children raise their hands to answer the questions. Ask individual children to explain the methods used for some of the questions.

1. 10 × 3
2. 4 multiplied by 5
3. double 7
4. the product of 4 and 4
5. 9 groups of 7
6. multiply 6 by 9
7. 4 lots of 8
8. 7 times 6
9. 3 × 4
10. double 3
11. the product of 8 and 3
12. multiply 5 by 9

Answers

1. 30
2. 20
3. 14
4. 16
5. 63
6. 54
7. 32
8. 42
9. 12
10. 6
11. 24
12. 45

5 Extending number bonds

Resources
A board or flipchart

Learning objective
Use efficient written methods to add and subtract whole numbers and decimals with up to two places.

Type of starter
Refine

Mental strategy
Addition: When adding the least significant digits and combining, discuss the need to start with the most significant digit first and read just the answer when a place value boundary is crossed. Also discuss the fact that decimal fractions behave in exactly the same way as whole numbers, as long as the decimal place is kept.

Subtraction: Discuss strategies for counting on to the next whole number or place value to find the difference, since decomposition methods are tricky to do mentally.

On the board write the following pairs of numbers: 5 and 3; 50 and 30; 500 and 300; 0.5 and 0.3. Ask the children to find the total and the difference for each pair. Ask: *How did the knowledge of the single-digit pair help you?*

Now write these two-digit pairs on the board:

1. 23 and 56
2. 18 and 28
3. 1.4 and 3.1
4. 2.7 and 1.4
5. 39 and 56
6. 0.16 and 0.11
7. 96 and 57
8. 8.5 and 6.9
9. 1.8 and 6.7
10. 4.9 and 5.2

Work through the first five examples together. Discuss the strategies used and the fact that known number bonds to 10 and a secure knowledge of place value support this type of mental addition and subtraction.

Ask the children to work in pairs to calculate the totals and differences for the remaining pairs of numbers, discussing their strategy as they work.

Answers

1. 79, 33
2. 46, 10
3. 4.5, 1.7
4. 4.1, 1.3
5. 95, 17
6. 0.27, 0.05
7. 153, 39
8. 15.4, 1.6
9. 8.5, 4.9
10. 10.1, 0.3

6 What comes next?

Learning objective
Count from any given number in whole-number and decimal steps, extending beyond zero when counting backwards; relate the numbers to their position on a number line.

Type of starter
Rehearse

Mental strategy
Encourage the children to work out the difference between the given numbers and to check with the next pair of numbers for accuracy.

Ensure that the children are able to explain that negative numbers appear to get numerically bigger, in that their distance away from zero increases, therefore they are actually 'smaller'.

Resources
A board or flipchart

Explain to the children that you are going to say a list of numbers and they are to raise their hand as soon as they recognise the pattern or the 'jumps' between the numbers. They must also tell you what comes next. Warn them that some of the patterns will increase in size, but some may decrease to below zero.

The whole class should begin the given number pattern again, passing it around the room, to give you the next six numbers in the pattern.

On the board, record the number patterns for all to see, ensuring that others can also explain the sequence pattern.

Suggested number patterns might be:

1. 25, 50, 75, ...
2. 35, 50, 65, ...
3. 13, 10, 7, ...
4. 420, 400, 380, ...
5. -11, -9, -7, -5, ...

Answers

1. 100, 125, 150, 175, 200
2. 80, 95, 110, 125, 140
3. 4, 1, -2, -5, -8
4. 360, 340, 320, 300, 280
5. -3, -1, 1, 3, 5

7 What factors?

Resources
A set of numeral cards 6–9 (from photocopiable page 89) for each child

Learning objective
Identify pairs of factors of two-digit whole numbers and find common multiples (eg for 6 and 9).

Type of starter
Recall

Answers

1. 6
2. 9
3. 7
4. 7
5. 6, 7
6. 6
7. 6, 9
8. 6, 8
9. 6, 8, 9
10. 7
11. 6, 9
12. 8
13. 6, 9
14. 7, 9

Ask: *In which times tables is 56 an answer?* Remind the children that 56 is a **multiple** of 8 and 7 because 7 × 8 = 56.

Explain that you are going to say a number that is a multiple of 6, 7, 8 or 9. The children should hold up the correct numeral card(s). Remind them that it might be a multiple of more than one number (for example, 18 is a multiple of both 6 and 9).

1. 30
2. 27
3. 49
4. 28
5. 42
6. 12
7. 36
8. 48
9. 72
10. 14
11. 90
12. 16
13. 54
14. 63

8 Ten times bigger

Resources
A board or flipchart; individual whiteboards and pens; place value arrow cards (from photocopiable pages 86, 87 and 88)

Learning objective
Use understanding of place value to multiply and divide whole numbers and decimals by 10, 100 or 1000.

Type of starter
Refine

No set answers

Ask the children to write on their whiteboards the number 7. Ask them to multiply it by 10 and write the answer. Ask: *What does it become? Now multiply it again by 10. And again.*

Ask them to think of other ways that they could have got from 7 to 7000. Encourage the children to explain the effect each time.

Model how the place value moves up one place, using arrow cards and the headings Th H T U on the board.

Repeat the process with the following numbers:

1. 3
2. 9
3. 0.5
4. 16
5. 27
6. 0.2

9 Venn Bingo sort

Learning objective
Explain reasoning using diagrams, graphs and text; refine ways of recording using images and symbols.

Type of starter
Reason

Resources
Individual whiteboards and pens; a 100 square

Ask the children to draw a Venn diagram with three intersecting rings. They should label the rings: Multiple of 5; Even number; Factor of 36.

Discuss the vocabulary to ensure understanding. Ask them to choose ten numbers from 1 to 50 and correctly place them onto the diagram, including numbers that fit the intersections, for example, 2 is a factor of 36 and an even number.

Explain that you will call out random numbers and if it matches one on their diagram, they should cross it out. The first person to cross out all of their numbers is the winner. Use the 100 square and cross out the numbers as you call them. Keeping a record like this allows you to check the claim. Children should be encouraged to explain their choice of placement.

No set answers

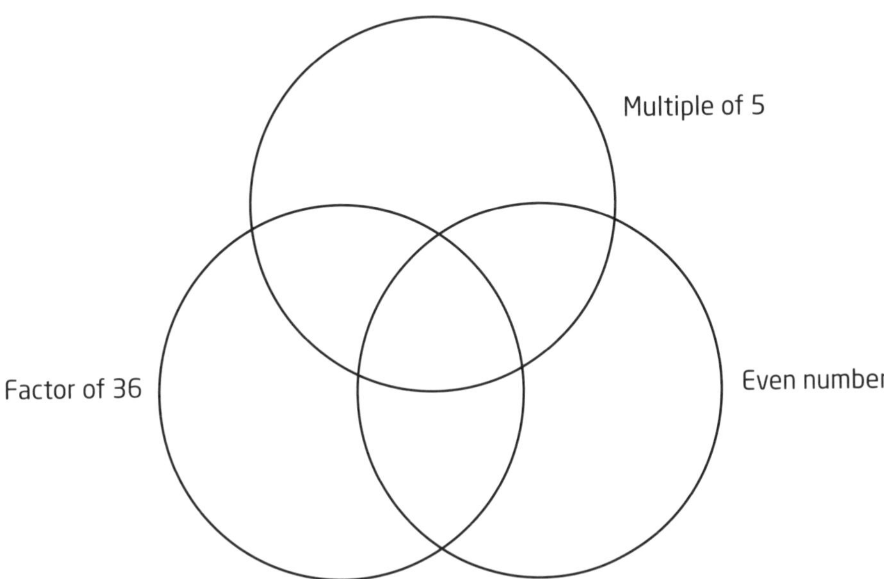

10 Halves around the room

Resources
None

Learning objective
Recall quickly multiplication facts up to 10 × 10 and use them to multiply pairs of multiples of 10 and 100; derive quickly corresponding division facts.

Type of starter
Recall

The children sit in a line or circle. The first child halves the start number, which is halved again by the second child, and so on. The first child to say a fraction correctly earns a point. A new start number is then given.

1. 80
2. 60
3. 72
4. 98
5. 64
6. 52
7. 100
8. 76
9. 88
10. 96
11. 68
12. 84

Answers

1. 40, 20, 10, 5, 2½
2. 30, 15, 7½
3. 36, 18, 9, 4½
4. 49, 24½
5. 32, 16, 8, 4, 2, 1, ½
6. 26, 13, 6½
7. 50, 25, 12½
8. 38, 19, 9½
9. 44, 22, 11, 5½
10. 48, 24, 12, 6, 3, 1½
11. 34, 17, 8½
12. 42, 21, 10½

11 Word problems Bingo

Learning objective
Solve one-step and two-step problems involving whole numbers and decimals and all four operations, choosing and using appropriate calculation strategies, including calculator use.

Type of starter
Reason

Mental strategy
Return to some of the questions and discuss the methods used.

Resources
Paper and a pencil for each child

The children should write down five numbers from 1 to 10 (inclusive), then cross them off if they are the answers to the questions. Make sure everyone knows the correct answers. The first child to cross out all five numbers wins.

To repeat the game, ask the questions in a different order.

1. One hundred pencils were put back into ten packets after being sharpened. How many pencils were in each packet?
2. A packet of six crayons costs 48p. How much is each crayon worth?
3. A net of 20 clementines was bought for £1.00. How much did each clementine cost?
4. Three packets of football cards gave me 18 cards altogether. How many are there in a packet?
5. There were four chocolate bars in a packet for three friends and me. How many bars did we have each?
6. We ran around the running track five times in 10 minutes. What was our average time for each lap?
7. I bought three CDs for £12. How much did each CD cost if they all cost the same?
8. We shared out the 42 conkers we had collected among six of us. How many each was that?
9. Thirty children in a PE lesson made ten groups. How many were there in each group?
10. There were 18 sweets in a packet. The children were to have two each. How many children were there?

Answers

1. 10
2. 8p
3. 5p
4. 6
5. 1
6. 2 minutes
7. £4
8. 7
9. 3
10. 9

BLOCK A

12 What's the question?

Resources
A board or flipchart

Learning objective
Recall quickly multiplication facts up to 10 × 10 and use them to multiply pairs of multiples of 10 and 100; derive quickly corresponding division facts.

Type of starter
Recall

Mental strategy
If the children have difficulty in making a division statement, remind them of the inverse nature of multiplication and division: 20 × 3 = 60 so 60 ÷ 3 = 20.

No set answers

Write on the board:

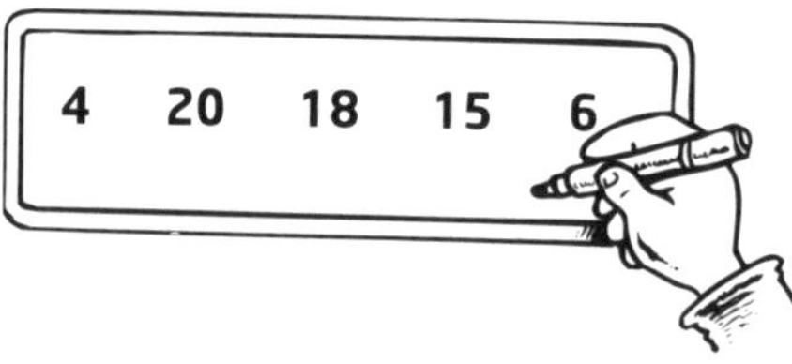

Ask the children to give multiplication or division questions that make each answer in turn. Build up a selection of questions for each answer. Encourage word problems too.

Unit 3

13 Building numbers

Resources
Six sets of numeral cards 1-9 (from photocopiable page 89); a large '0' card

Learning objective
Explain what each digit represents in whole numbers and decimals with up to two places, and partition, round and order these numbers.

Type of starter
Refine

Answers

1. 200
2. 8000
3. 1
4. 20
5. 10,000
6. 800,000
7. 90
8. 50,000
9. 2
10. 600,000

Select one child to be the 'zero'. He or she will be placed where needed. Divide the class into two groups, the 'Thousands' and the 'Ones'. Subdivide each group into 'Hundreds', 'Tens' and 'Units'. Deal a set of numeral cards among each of the six subgroups.

Build each large number (one digit at a time), with children standing together holding their cards, for example, 2 units, 5 tens, 3 hundreds. All say: 'Three hundred and fifty-two'. Continue with the 'Thousands' group: 4 units, 7 tens, 1 hundred. All say: 'One hundred and seventy-four thousand, three hundred and fifty-two.' Ask for the value of the number in brackets.

1. 486,213 (2)
2. 748,609 (8)
3. 527,431 (1)
4. 103,928 (2)
5. 219,374 (1)
6. 831,547 (8)
7. 370,895 (9)
8. 952,760 (5)
9. 764,052 (2)
10. 695,183 (6)

Decimal pairs

Learning objective
Use knowledge of place value and addition and subtraction of two-digit numbers to derive sums and differences and doubles and halves of decimals (eg 6.5 ± 2.7, half of 5.6, double 0.34).

Type of starter
Rehearse

Mental strategy
Remind the children to use their number bonds to 10, taking into account any numbers that 'bridge' from the tenths to the units. For example, the 'tenths' need to add up to 10, but the 'units' only need make 9 to allow for the 'carried' digit.

Resources
A set of numeral cards 0–9 (from photocopiable page 89) for each pair; whiteboards and pens

Each pair generates a number by choosing two numeral cards and sticking them onto a whiteboard with a decimal point drawn in between to make a decimal number, for example 3.7. The first of the pair to say the decimal number that will make 10 when added to the generated number gains a point. Record points as a tally chart on the board. The pair must check and agree that the answer is correct. Repeat until someone scores 10 points.

No set answers

Division Bingo

Learning objective
Recall quickly multiplication facts up to 10 × 10 and use them to multiply pairs of multiples of 10 and 100; derive quickly corresponding division facts.

Type of starter
Recall

Resources
Paper and a pencil for each child

The children write six numbers between 1 and 10 (inclusive). They cross a number off when it is the answer to a question. The first to cross out all numbers wins. Repeat each game, asking questions in a different order.

Game 1
1. 63 divided by 7
2. 8 divided by 8
3. How many 6s in 42?
4. Divide 21 by 7
5. The quotient of 54 and 9
6. How many 8s in 32?
7. 90 divided by 9
8. Divide 12 by 6
9. One-eighth of 64
10. 35 divided by 7

Game 2
11. 27 divided by 9
12. How many 6s in 30?
13. One-eighth of 16
14. Divide 72 by 9
15. Divide 28 by 7
16. The quotient of 48 and 8
17. 6 divided by 6
18. How many 9s in 81?
19. 60 divided by 6
20. How many 7s in 49?

Answers

Game 1		Game 2	
1.	9	11.	3
2.	1	12.	5
3.	7	13.	2
4.	3	14.	8
5.	6	15.	4
6.	4	16.	6
7.	10	17.	1
8.	2	18.	9
9.	8	19.	10
10.	5	20.	7

16 Order! Order!

Resources
A board or flipchart; individual whiteboards and pens

Learning objective
Count from any given number in whole-number and decimal steps, extending beyond zero when counting backwards; relate the numbers to their position on a number line.

Type of starter
Recall

Write the following lists of numbers on to the board. Ask the children to look very carefully, since some of the lists contain both positive and negative numbers and some contain decimals. They must rewrite each list in ascending size order.

1. 48, 44, 24, 104, 49, 14, 40
2. -9, -21, -19, 17, 3, -11, 8
3. 2.3, -5, -2, 2, 1.1, 0.2, 0.5
4. -19, -18, -2, -8, -20, 2, 0
5. -10, -11, 1, 5, -9, 2, 0
6. 0.99, 1, 1.1, 0.89, 0, 1.5
7. -3, -30, 30, 3, 33, -23, -20
8. 36, -2, 89, 46, -1, 28, 1
9. 23, 24, 0.2, -2, 2, 22, 3
10. -9, -10, -13, -4, -7, -8, 0

Answers

1. 14, 24, 40, 44, 48, 49, 104
2. -21, -19, -11, -9, 3, 8, 17
3. -5, -2, 0.2, 0.5, 1.1, 2, 2.3
4. -20, -19, -18, -8, -2, 0, 2
5. -11, -10, -9, 0, 1, 2, 5
6. 0.89, 0.99, 0, 1, 1.1, 1.5
7. -30, -23, -20, -3, 3, 30, 33
8. -2, -1, 1, 28, 36, 46, 89
9. -2, 0.2, 2, 3, 22, 23, 24
10. -13, -10, -9, -8, -7, -4, 0

Summer-fair problems

Learning objective
Solve one-step and two-step problems involving whole numbers and decimals and all four operations, choosing and using appropriate calculation strategies, including calculator use.

Type of starter
Rehearse

Mental strategy
Discuss with the children their decision making processes and how they managed to maximise the choices that the children made in order to get best value for their £5.00. Encourage them to look for ways in which to combine amounts easily, eg 3 × 30p, or making whole pounds, eg £1.25 + £1.75, for ease of calculation.

Resources
A board or flipchart; individual whiteboards or paper and pencils

Copy the following information about summer fair activity prices on to the board.

At the summer fair, activities were priced as follows:

- table top games 50p
- all races £1.00 entry each race
- sweets 30p
- pony rides £1.75
- roundabout rides £1.25.

Three children, Jane, Tom and Amyas, were each given £5.00 to spend. They all went on at least three different things.

- Jane hates sports and races.
- Tom is allergic to animals.
- Amyas is very competitive and likes to win things.

Suggest ways in which each child might have chosen to spend their money, bringing home the least change possible. Explain your choices.

How much change did each child bring home?

No set answers

18 Approximations

Resources
A board or flipchart; an OHP calculator; individual whiteboards or pencils and paper for each pair

Learning objective
Use knowledge of rounding, place value, number facts and inverse operations to estimate and check calculations.

Type of starter
Reason

Mental strategy
Encourage the children to estimate by approximating (round to 10 or 100). They should then check their result.

Answers
1. 308 + 205
2. 675 + 122
3. 155 + 122
4. 770 + 122
5. 430 + 155

6. 360 - 155
7. 910 - 205
8. 770 - 360
9. 770 - 675
10. 450 - 155

Write on the board (well spaced out):

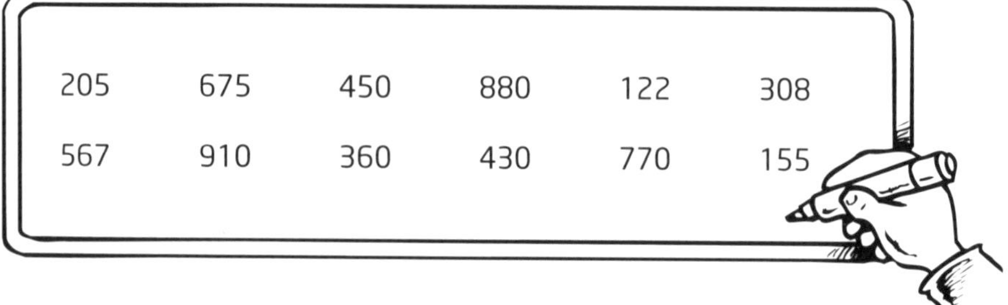

Ask pairs of children to choose two numbers from the board that add/subtract to give a number closest to the given number. Emphasise that rounding the numbers will be useful.

Collect several suggestions and decide which pair is nearest (use an OHP or whiteboard calculator to demonstrate).

Total of about:

1. 500
2. 800
3. 300
4. 900
5. 600

Difference of about:

6. 200
7. 700
8. 400
9. 100
10. 300

BLOCK B

Unit 1

	100 Mental Maths Starters			100 Maths Lessons		
Page	**Objective**	**Activity title**	**Starter type**	**Unit**	**Lesson**	**Page**
23	Recall quickly multiplication facts up to 10 × 10 and use them to multiply pairs of multiples of 10 and 100; derive quickly corresponding division facts.	19 Guess my number	Recall	1	1	50
23	Recall quickly multiplication facts up to 10 × 10 and use them to multiply pairs of multiples of 10 and 100; derive quickly corresponding division facts.	20 Tables snap	Recall	1	2	58
24	Recall quickly multiplication facts up to 10 × 10 and use them to multiply pairs of multiples of 10 and 100; derive quickly corresponding division facts.	21 Ten lots of division	Refine	1	3	59
24	Identify, visualise and describe properties of rectangles, triangles, regular polygons and 3D solids; use knowledge of properties to draw 2D shapes and identify and draw nets of 3D shapes.	22 Guess the shape (1)	Recall	1	4	50
25	Identify pairs of factors of two-digit whole numbers and find common multiples (eg for 6 and 9).	23 Factor facts	Refine	1	7	54
26	Explore patterns, properties and relationships and propose a general statement involving numbers or shapes; identify examples for which the statement is true or false.	24 Odd one out	Rehearse	1	8	55
26	Use knowledge of rounding, place value, number facts and inverse operations to estimate and check calculations.	25 Estimating answers	Rehearse	1	10	56
27	Identify, visualise and describe properties of rectangles, triangles, regular polygons and 3D solids; use knowledge of properties to draw 2D shapes and identify and draw nets of 3D shapes.	26 Shape descriptions	Reason	1	11	57

Unit 2

	100 Mental Maths Starters			100 Maths Lessons		
Page	**Objective**	**Activity title**	**Starter type**	**Unit**	**Lesson**	**Page**
28	Recall quickly multiplication facts up to 10 × 10 and use them to multiply pairs of multiples of 10 and 100; derive quickly corresponding division facts.	27 Fast times	Recall	2	1	66
28	Use knowledge of place value and addition and subtraction of two-digit numbers to derive sums and differences and doubles and halves of decimals (eg 6.5 ± 2.7, half of 5.6, double 0.34).	28 Doubling around the room	Rehearse	2	3	67

Unit 2 ...continued

100 Mental Maths Starters				100 Maths Lessons		
Page	Objective	Activity title	Starter type	Unit	Lesson	Page
29	Use knowledge of rounding, place value, number facts and inverse operations to estimate and check calculations.	29 What's the question?	Refine	2	5	72
29	Recall quickly multiplication facts up to 10 × 10 and use them to multiply pairs of multiples of 10 and 100; derive quickly corresponding division facts.	30 Sixes and sevens	Recall	2	6	69
30	Recall quickly multiplication facts up to 10 × 10 and use them to multiply pairs of multiples of 10 and 100; derive quickly corresponding division facts.	31 Follow me	Rehearse	2	8	70
30	Recall quickly multiplication facts up to 10 × 10 and use them to multiply pairs of multiples of 10 and 100; derive quickly corresponding division facts.	32 Multiplication and division	Rehearse	2	9	71
31	Use knowledge of place value and addition and subtraction of two-digit numbers to derive sums and differences and doubles and halves of decimals (eg 6.5 ± 2.7, half of 5.6, double 0.34).	33 Pairs to make 1	Rehearse	2	14	75
32	Recall quickly multiplication facts up to 10 × 10 and use them to multiply pairs of multiples of 10 and 100; derive quickly corresponding division facts.	34 Divisibility vote	Recall	2	15	75

Unit 3

100 Mental Maths Starters				100 Maths Lessons		
Page	Objective	Activity title	Starter type	Unit	Lesson	Page
32	Use knowledge of place value and addition and subtraction of two-digit numbers to derive sums and differences and doubles and halves of decimals (eg 6.5 ± 2.7, half of 5.6, double 0.34).	35 Pairs to make 10	Rehearse	3	1	82
33	Recall quickly multiplication facts up to 10 × 10 and use them to multiply pairs of multiples of 10 and 100; derive quickly corresponding division facts.	36 Matching answers	Recall	3	3	83
34	Recall quickly multiplication facts up to 10 × 10 and use them to multiply pairs of multiples of 10 and 100; derive quickly corresponding division facts.	37 Tables snap	Recall	3	4	85
35	Use a calculator to solve problems, including those involving decimals or fractions (eg to find ¾ of 150g); interpret the display correctly in the context of measurement.	38 Calculator conversion	Rehearse	3	5	86
36	Use knowledge of place value and addition and subtraction of two-digit numbers to derive sums and differences and doubles and halves of decimals (eg 6.5 ± 2.7, half of 5.6, double 0.34).	39 Double dash	Refine	3	7	87
36	Use knowledge of rounding, place value, number facts and inverse operations to estimate and check calculations.	40 Take it in parts	Rehearse	3	11	89
37	Derive quickly all pairs of multiples of 50 with a total of 1000.	41 Kilograms and grams	Rehearse	3	13	91
37	Identify, visualise and describe properties of rectangles, triangles, regular polygons and 3D solids; use knowledge of properties to draw 2D shapes and identify and draw nets of 3D shapes.	42 Guess the shape (2)	Reason	3	14	92

19 Guess my number

Learning objective
Recall quickly multiplication facts up to 10 × 10 and use them to multiply pairs of multiples of 10 and 100; derive quickly corresponding division facts.

Type of starter
Recall

Resources
None

Children should raise their hands to answer the following questions.

1. 5 multiplied by 4.
2. 9 times 3.
3. Double 8.
4. This number is a multiple of 2 and 5, and is less than 12.
5. Multiply 10 by 6.
6. What is the product of 3 and 8?
7. Double 6.
8. This even number is a multiple of 2, 3, 5 and 10 and is less than 40.
9. This multiple of 3 is 1 less than 10.
10. This multiple of 10 is between 65 and 75.

Answers

1. 20
2. 27
3. 16
4. 10
5. 60
6. 24
7. 12
8. 30
9. 9
10. 70

20 Tables snap

Learning objective
Recall quickly multiplication facts up to 10 × 10 and use them to multiply pairs of multiples of 10 and 100; derive quickly corresponding division facts.

Type of starter
Recall

Resources
Two or three sets of Snap cards (enlarged from photocopiable page 90 and cut out)

Give each child a Snap card (more confident children could be given extra cards).

The children who have the answer to a question should hold up the card and say 'Snap'.

The children can swap cards with a neighbour to repeat the game.

1. 6 × 2
2. 8 × 3
3. 6 × 5
4. 8 × 2
5. 9 × 3
6. 5 × 5
7. 7 × 3
8. 6 × 4
9. 7 × 5
10. 9 × 4
11. 6 × 3
12. 8 × 5
13. 7 × 2
14. 4 × 5
15. 9 × 2
16. 8 × 4
17. 9 × 5
18. 7 × 4

Answers

1. 12
2. 24
3. 30
4. 16
5. 27
6. 25
7. 21
8. 24
9. 35
10. 36
11. 18
12. 40
13. 14
14. 20
15. 18
16. 32
17. 45
18. 28

BLOCK B

21 Ten lots of division

Resources
A board or flipchart

Learning objective
Recall quickly multiplication facts up to 10 × 10 and use them to multiply pairs of multiples of 10 and 100; derive quickly corresponding division facts.

Type of starter
Refine

No set answers

On the board or flipchart write the number 12. Ask the children to identify the times tables that would make the number 12, for example 2 × 6, 3 × 4 and so on. Arrange these as a 'starburst' around the number.

Now write the number 120. Ask the children to tell you the factors of this number based on their known times tables, but using multiples of 10, for example 20 × 6, 60 × 2, 30 × 4, 40 × 3. Demonstrate why they cannot have 30 × 40, since this is a multiple of 100. Record in the same way.

Ask the children to do the same with:

150 240 360 160 180 320 300 420 1800 2400

22 Guess the shape (1)

Resources
A set of cut-out shapes (enlarged from photocopiable page 92); a cloth bag or cardboard box

Learning objective
Identify, visualise and describe properties of rectangles, triangles, regular polygons and 3D solids; use knowledge of properties to draw 2D shapes and identify and draw nets of 3D shapes.

Type of starter
Recall

No set answers

The children, individually or with a partner, must pick a shape from the pile and describe it to the rest of the class.

They should keep the shape hidden in a bag or box. The class try to guess what shape it is.

If the class need to ask for more information, their questions must be answerable with 'Yes' or 'No'.

Encourage them not to try to guess what the shape is until they have gathered enough information to be sure.

Remind them of the questions that could be asked:

- *How many sides?*
- *How many corners?*
- *How many right angles?*

23 Factor facts

Learning objective
Identify pairs of factors of two-digit whole numbers and find common multiples (eg for 6 and 9).

Type of starter
Refine

Resources
A board or flipchart; individual whiteboard and pens

Using a Venn diagram of only two rings, identify the factors of two given numbers and find the common factors, for example:

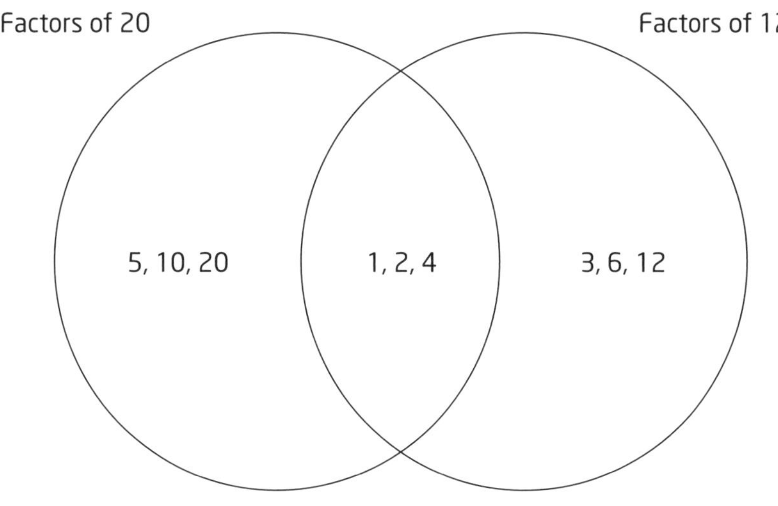

In pairs, ask the children to find the factors from the following pairs of numbers and to identify the ones common to both.

1. 12 and 15
2. 20 and 18
3. 18 and 30
4. 24 and 30
5. 32 and 42

Answers

(Common factors in bold)

1. 12: (**1**, 2, **3**, 4, 6, 12)

   15: (**1**, **3**, 5, 15)
2. 20: (**1**, **2**, 4, 5, 10, 20)

   18: (**1**, **2**, 3, 6, 9, 18)
3. 18: (**1**, **2**, **3**, **6**, 9, 18)

   30: (**1**, **2**, **3**, 5, **6**, 10, 15, 30)
4. 24: (**1**, **2**, **3**, 4, **6**, 8, 12, 24)

   30: (**1**, **2**, **3**, 5, **6**, 10, 15, 30)
5. 32: (**1**, **2**, 4, 8, 16, 32)

   42: (**1**, **2**, 3, 6, 7, 14, 21, 42)

Odd one out

Resources
A board or flipchart

Learning objective
Explore patterns, properties and relationships and propose a general statement involving numbers or shapes; identify examples for which the statement is true or false.

Type of starter
Rehearse

Answers

1. 17 (even numbers)
2. 16 (multiples of 5)
3. 12 (square numbers)
4. 4 (odd numbers)
5. 14 (multiples of 4)
6. 6 (factors of 100)
7. 35 (multiples of 3)
8. 5 (factors of 42)

On the board, randomly write the following sets of numbers, asking the children to identify which number is the 'Odd one out' in each group and to explain why.

1.	12 17 2 8 104 40 20 200	2.	20 100 15 16 35 250 40 80	3.	9 4 100 25 49 81 64 12	4.	4 13 27 19 3 105 11 37
5.	400 40 4 24 32 16 14 36	6.	5 25 20 100 4 6 50 2	7.	18 12 3 30 15 27 35 21	8.	2 3 5 6 7 14 21 42

25 Estimating answers

Resources
Paper, a pencil and three dice for each pair

Learning objective
Use knowledge of rounding, place value, number facts and inverse operations to estimate and check calculations.

Type of starter
Rehearse

No set answers

Split the class into mixed-ability pairs. They must roll their three dice to produce three digits, write them down and arrange them as a TU × U calculation to produce an answer that can be rounded to the given multiple of 100. For example: 5, 4 and 3 → 43 × 5 = 215, which rounds to 200.

If they succeed, they score a point. The first pair to reach 4 points wins. Encourage the children to explain any strategies they have developed. The game can then start over again.

1.	200	4.	300	7.	400	10.	300
2.	100	5.	100	8.	200	11.	100
3.	200	6.	200	9.	100	12.	200

(26) Shape descriptions

Learning objective
Identify, visualise and describe properties of rectangles, triangles, regular polygons and 3D solids; use knowledge of properties to draw 2D shapes and identify and draw nets of 3D shapes.

Type of starter
Reason

Resources
None

Read out each shape description, pause, then give a silent signal. The children should raise their hands if they can answer.

If time allows, individuals can describe a shape for the class to guess.

1. It has four sides and four right angles.
   The opposite sides are parallel.
   The four sides are of equal length.
2. This polygon has five angles of equal size.
   Its five diagonals do not bisect each other.
   It has five sides of equal length.
3. It is a closed curve.
   It does not have sides.
   Every point on the curve is an equal distance from the centre.
   A straight line through its centre from one point on the curve to another point is called a diameter.
4. It has no diagonals.
   It has three equal sides and three equal angles.
5. It is a quadrilateral.
   Not all the sides are the same length.
   The opposite sides are parallel.
   Each vertex measures 90°.
   It has two diagonals, which bisect each other.
   The opposite sides are of equal length.

Answers

1. square
2. regular pentagon
3. circle
4. equilateral triangle
5. rectangle (oblong)

27 Fast times

Resources
None

Learning objective
Recall quickly multiplication facts up to 10 × 10 and use them to multiply pairs of multiples of 10 and 100; derive quickly corresponding division facts.

Type of starter
Recall

Answers

1.	8	11.	12
2.	30	12.	24
3.	27	13.	15
4.	16	14.	10
5.	21	15.	32
6.	90	16.	42
7.	28	17.	12
8.	12	18.	30
9.	16	19.	35
10.	50	20.	20

Read out these questions for a quick recall test. Ask the children to raise a hand if they know the answer.

1.	4 × 2	11.	2 × 6
2.	6 × 5	12.	6 × 4
3.	3 × 9	13.	5 × 3
4.	2 × 8	14.	2 × 5
5.	7 × 3	15.	4 × 8
6.	10 × 9	16.	7 × 6
7.	4 × 7	17.	6 × 2
8.	3 × 4	18.	3 × 10
9.	8 × 2	19.	5 × 7
10.	5 × 10	20.	4 × 5

28 Doubling around the room

Resources
None

Learning objective
Use knowledge of place value and addition and subtraction of two-digit numbers to derive sums and differences and doubles and halves of decimals (eg 6.5 ± 2.7, half of 5.6, double 0.34).

Type of starter
Rehearse

Answers

1. 0.2, 0.4, 0.8, 1.6, 3.2, 6.4, 12.8
2. 1.1, 2.2, 4.4, 8.8, 17.6
3. 0.7, 1.4, 2.8, 5.6, 11.2
4. 1.3, 2.6, 5.2, 10.4
5. 0.9, 1.8, 3.6, 7.2, 14.4

Divide the class into five or six groups.

The first group doubles a given decimal number, the second group doubles it again, and so on until a group can say 'Over 10' to earn a point. The team with the most points at the end wins.

1. 0.2
2. 1.1
3. 0.7
4. 1.3
5. 0.9

29 What's the question?

Learning objective
Use knowledge of rounding, place value, number facts and inverse operations to estimate and check calculations.

Type of starter
Refine

Resources
A board or flipchart; paper and pencils for each pair

Write on the board:

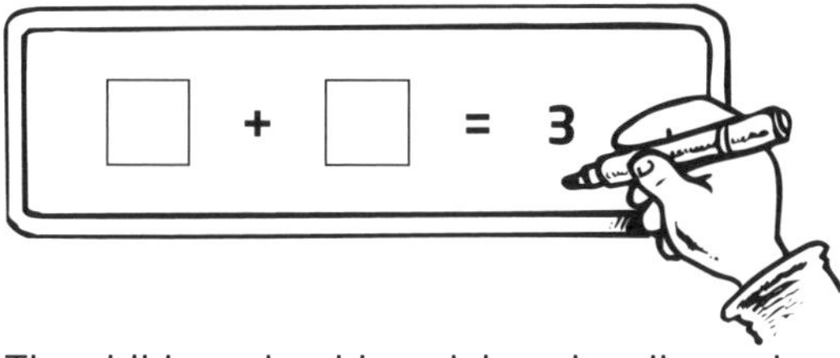

The children should work in pairs, discussing what the numbers could be. Write some of their suggestions on the board and discuss ways of checking them (for example, using inverse operations). Let them go on to try these:

1. □ ÷ □ = 3
2. □ ÷ □ = 7
3. □ ÷ □ = 1
4. □ ÷ □ = 25
5. □ ÷ □ = 40
6. □ ÷ □ = 9

No set answers

30 Sixes and sevens

Learning objective
Recall quickly multiplication facts up to 10 × 10 and use them to multiply pairs of multiples of 10 and 100; derive quickly corresponding division facts.

Type of starter
Recall

Resources
A large multiplication square displayed on an interactive whiteboard or OHP

Display the multiplication square.

Ask individual children to highlight multiples of 6 in one colour and multiples of 7 in a different colour.

Point out that 42 is a multiple of both 6 and 7.

When all the multiples have been highlighted, chant the numbers for each times table.

1. 3 × 6
2. 5 × 7
3. 6 × 6
4. 2 × 7
5. 4 × 6
6. 3 × 7
7. 5 × 6
8. 4 × 7
9. 7 × 6
10. 9 × 6

Answers

1. 18
2. 35
3. 36
4. 14
5. 24
6. 21
7. 30
8. 28
9. 42
10. 54

31 Follow me

Resources
'Follow me' cards (from photocopiable page 93)

Learning objective
Recall quickly multiplication facts up to 10 × 10 and use them to multiply pairs of multiples of 10 and 100; derive quickly corresponding division facts.

Type of starter
Rehearse

No set answers

Deal out the 32 'Follow me' cards. All of the cards need to be in play, so more confident children could be given more than one card if necessary.

Choose a child to ask the question on his or her card. The child who has the answer in a circle on his or her card says it clearly, then says the calculation on that card. This carries on until the game loops back to the first player.

If more than 32 cards are needed, the extra six cards shown below could be made. The answer on the '3 × 4' card will then need to be changed to '20'.

32 Multiplication and division

Resources
None

Learning objective
Recall quickly multiplication facts up to 10 × 10 and use them to multiply pairs of multiples of 10 and 100; derive quickly corresponding division facts.

Type of starter
Rehearse

Answers

1. 12
2. 42
3. 6
4. 5
5. 72
6. 48
7. 28
8. 9
9. 6
10. 5

Ask for quick responses to the following questions. Children should raise a hand if they know the answer or write the answers on individual whiteboards.

1. 2 × 6
2. 6 × 7
3. 18 ÷ 3
4. 40 ÷ 8
5. What is the product of 9 and 8?
6. There are eight sweets in each packet. How many in six packets?
7. Halve 56
8. The children sat in rows of 10. How many rows would 90 children fill?
9. Some drinks cartons were wrapped in packets of six. How many packets would be needed, for each child in a class of 34 children, to have one each?
10. What is the quotient of 35 and 7?

33 Pairs to make 1

Learning objective
Use knowledge of place value and addition and subtraction of two-digit numbers to derive sums and differences and doubles and halves of decimals (eg 6.5 ± 2.7, half of 5.6, double 0.34).

Type of starter
Rehearse

Mental strategy
Encourage the children to understand that when we write whole numbers, the decimal point does not need to be shown because there are no decimal figures.

Resources
A board or flipchart

Write on the board:

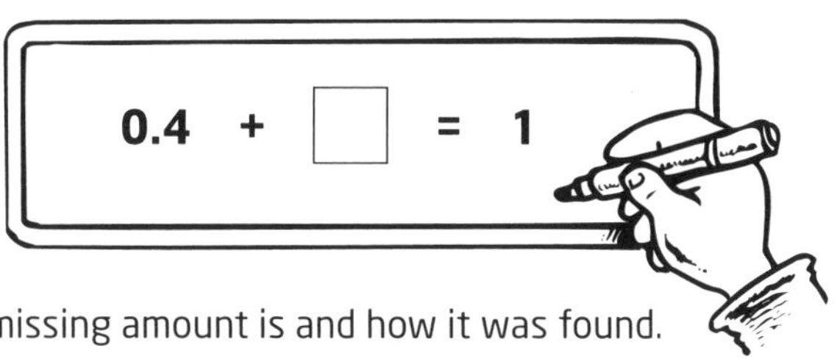

Ask what the missing amount is and how it was found.

Practise quick recall of pairs making 10. For example: *I say 7, you say...* The children say the answers together.

1. 7
2. 5
3. 2
4. 9
5. 4
6. 3
7. 8
8. 1
9. 6

Discuss the position of the decimal point in 1 unit. Ask: *Why does it not need to be shown?* Practise quick recall of pairs to make 1, as above.

10. 0.6
11. 0.9
12. 0.3

Answers

1. 3
2. 5
3. 8
4. 1
5. 6
6. 7
7. 2
8. 9
9. 4
10. 0.4
11. 0.1
12. 0.7

Unit 2

34 Divisibility vote

Resources
A board or flipchart

Learning objective
Recall quickly multiplication facts up to 10 × 10 and use them to multiply pairs of multiples of 10 and 100; derive quickly corresponding division facts.

Type of starter
Recall

Mental strategy
Multiples of 2 and 4 are always even. Numbers divisible by 4 are also divisible by 2, but not vice versa.

Multiples of 5 always end in 0 or 5. Numbers divisible by 10 are also divisible by 5, but not necessarily the opposite way round.

Multiples of 10 end in 0; multiples of 100 end in 00. Numbers divisible by 100 are also divisible by 10, but not vice versa.

Write on the board the number 265. Explain to the children that they have to decide whether this number is divisible by 2, 4, 5, 10 or 100 and to explain their reasoning. (It is divisible only by 5.)

Repeat with:

1. 76
2. 4000
3. 120
4. 170
5. 152
6. 116
7. 9050

Answers

1. 2, 4
2. 10, 100
3. 2, 4, 5, 10
4. 2, 5, 10
5. 2, 4
6. 2, 4
7. 2, 5, 10

Unit 3

35 Pairs to make 10

Resources
None

Learning objective
Use knowledge of place value and addition and subtraction of two-digit numbers to derive sums and differences and doubles and halves of decimals (eg 6.5 ± 2.7, half of 5.6, double 0.34).

Type of starter
Rehearse

Say the decimal number and ask how much more needs to be added to make 10. Encourage complementary addition.

1. 4.0
2. 9.0
3. 2.0
4. 8.5
5. 6.5
6. 7.8
7. 9.2
8. 3.6
9. 5.1
10. 2.7
11. 4.3
12. 1.9
13. 8.4
14. 3.5
15. 6.0

Answers

1. 6.0
2. 1.0
3. 8.0
4. 1.5
5. 3.5
6. 2.2
7. 0.8
8. 6.4
9. 4.9
10. 7.3
11. 5.7
12. 8.1
13. 1.6
14. 6.5
15. 4.0

(36) Matching answers

Learning objective
Recall quickly multiplication facts up to 10 × 10 and use them to multiply pairs of multiples of 10 and 100; derive quickly corresponding division facts.

Type of starter
Recall

Resources
A board or flipchart

Write the following on the board, well spaced out:

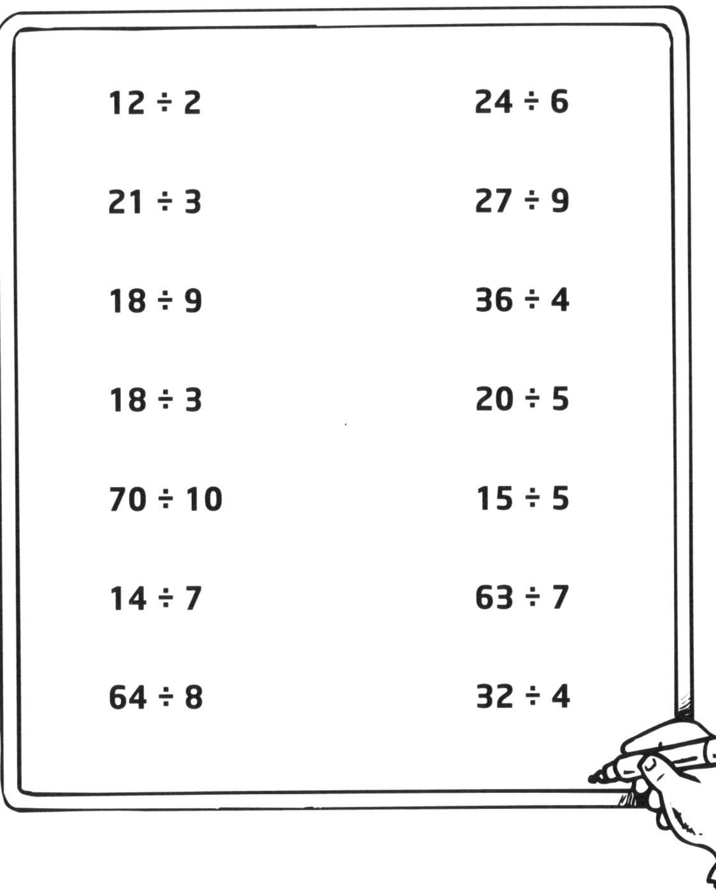

Give the children a few minutes to work out the answers. They should work quietly in pairs or threes (not necessarily of similar ability).

Ask for pairs of divisions that give the same answer. Join these with a line. When the divisions have all been matched up, point to one division and ask the children to give a different division statement with the same answer. Discuss their methods.

No set answers

BLOCK B

37 Tables snap

Resources
Two or more sets of Snap cards (enlarged from photocopiable page 91)

Learning objective
Recall quickly multiplication facts up to 10 × 10 and use them to multiply pairs of multiples of 10 and 100; derive quickly corresponding division facts.

Type of starter
Recall

Answers
1. 42
2. 21
3. 40
4. 56
5. 54
6. 63
7. 36
8. 28
9. 64
10. 18
11. 35
12. 24
13. 81
14. 32
15. 30
16. 49
17. 72
18. 27
19. 48
20. 45

Deal a Snap card to each child. Explain that they should hold it up and say 'Snap' when it is the answer to a question. More confident children could have an extra card.

To replay the game, children could swap cards with a neighbour.

1. 7 × 6
2. 3 × 7
3. 5 × 8
4. 8 × 7
5. 9 × 6
6. 7 × 9
7. 6 × 6
8. 4 × 7
9. 8 × 8
10. 3 × 6
11. 5 × 7
12. 4 × 6
13. 9 × 9
14. 4 × 8
15. 5 × 6
16. 7 × 7
17. 8 × 9
18. 3 × 9
19. 6 × 8
20. 5 × 9

38 Calculator conversion

Learning objective
Use a calculator to solve problems, including those involving decimals or fractions (eg to find ¾ of 150g); interpret the display correctly in the context of measurement.

Type of starter
Rehearse

Mental strategy
Conversions: 1kg = 1000g; 1km = 1000m; 1 litre = 1000ml; 1m = 100cm
To convert from a larger unit of measure to a smaller, multiply (for example 4.5km × 1000 = 4500m) and to convert a smaller to a larger unit, divide (for example 650cm ÷ 100 = 6.5m).

Resources
A board or flipchart; calculators; individual whiteboards and pens

Ask questions about changing units of measure to larger equivalents. Give the children time to answer each question on their individual whiteboards.

	Amount	Convert to
1.	4kg	g
2.	2.5kg	g
3.	7300g	kg
4.	750cm	m
5.	5m	cm
6.	2500ml	l
7.	6.4 litres	ml
8.	12.4km	m
9.	36,000m	km
10.	1250cm	m

Next, give each child a calculator and explain that they are going to use them to check their answers.

Answers
1. 4000g
2. 2500g
3. 7.3kg
4. 7.5m
5. 500cm
6. 2.5l
7. 6400ml
8. 12,400m
9. 36km
10. 12.5m

39 Double dash

Resources
A board or flipchart

Learning objective
Use knowledge of place value and addition and subtraction of two-digit numbers to derive sums and differences and doubles and halves of decimals (eg 6.5 ± 2.7, half of 5.6, double 0.34).

Type of starter
Refine

Answers

1.	16.2	11.	32.4
2.	28.4	12.	23.6
3.	7.2	13.	30.8
4.	19	14.	48.8
5.	10.4	15.	35.6
6.	1.2	16.	34.2
7.	2.8	17.	13.8
8.	14.8	18.	42.8
9.	11.8	19.	19.2
10.	28.8	20.	22

Explain to the children that they are going to be using their knowledge of doubling to multiply decimals by 2 or 4. Remind them that multiplying by 4 may be achieved quickly by doubling and doubling again.

Divide the class into two teams for a quick-fire competition. The first team to answer your question correctly gains a point. The first to 10 points wins.

1. double 8.1
2. 7.1 × 4
3. double 3.6
4. double 9.5
5. 2.6 × 4
6. double 0.6
7. 0.7 × 4
8. 3.7 × 4
9. double 5.9
10. 7.2 × 4
11. double 16.2
12. double 11.8
13. 7.7 × 4
14. 12.2 × 4
15. 8.9 × 4
16. double 17.1
17. double 6.9
18. double 21.4
19. 4.8 × 4
20. 5.5 × 4

40 Take it in parts

Resources
Number fan for each child

Learning objective
Use knowledge of rounding, place value, number facts and inverse operations to estimate and check calculations.

Type of starter
Rehearse

Mental strategy
Encourage the children to partition the two-digit number and multiply the most significant digit first. This way is easier to hold in their head.

Answers

1.	60	6.	138
2.	108	7.	153
3.	76	8.	72
4.	160	9.	168
5.	128	10.	210

Explain that you are going to ask some TU × U multiplication questions. The children should display the answer on their number fans.

1. 12 × 5
2. 18 × 6
3. 19 × 4
4. 32 × 5
5. 16 × 8
6. 23 × 6
7. 17 × 9
8. 24 × 3
9. 21 × 8
10. 42 × 5

41 Kilograms and grams

Learning objective
Derive quickly all pairs of multiples of 50 with a total of 1000.

Type of starter
Rehearse

Mental strategy
Remind the children that 1000 grams equal 1 kilogram.

Resources
None

Ask: *If 750 grams of flour have been used from a 1 kilogram bag, how much will be left?*

How many more to 1000g from:

1. 700g
2. 900g
3. 400g
4. 600g
5. 300g
6. 500g

How many grams are left after taking from 1000g:

7. 850g
8. 200g
9. 450g
10. 750g
11. 100g
12. 350g
13. 800g
14. 950g
15. 250g

Answers

1. 300g
2. 100g
3. 600g
4. 400g
5. 700g
6. 500g
7. 150g
8. 800g
9. 550g
10. 250g
11. 900g
12. 650g
13. 200g
14. 50g
15. 750g

42 Guess the shape (2)

Learning objective
Identify, visualise and describe properties of rectangles, triangles, regular polygons and 3D solids; use knowledge of properties to draw 2D shapes and identify and draw nets of 3D shapes.

Type of starter
Reason

Mental strategy
Encourage the children, when they are guessing, not to say what the shape is until they have enough information to be sure.

Resources
Two sets of shape cards (enlarged from photocopiable page 92)

Discuss with the children what questions they could ask to help them guess what shape someone is holding. Only the answers 'Yes' and 'No' are allowed. For example: *Does it have three sides? Are the sides of equal length? Are all the angles equal?*

Divide the class into pairs or groups of three. Deal each group a shape card, face down. Each group must answer questions from the class until their shape is guessed correctly. To repeat, collect the cards and deal them again.

No set answers

BLOCK C

BLOCK C

Unit 1

	100 Mental Maths Starters			100 Maths Lessons		
Page	**Objective**	**Activity title**	**Starter type**	**Unit**	**Lesson**	**Page**
40	Extend mental methods for whole-number calculations.	(43) Maths in minutes	Refresh	1	2	100
40	Read, choose, use and record standard metric units to estimate and measure length, weight and capacity to a suitable degree of accuracy (eg the nearest centimetre); convert larger to smaller units using decimals to one place (eg change 2.6kg to 2600g).	(44) Units of weight	Refresh	1	3	101
41	Explain reasoning using diagrams, graphs and text; refine ways of recording using images and symbols.	(45) Picture this!	Reason	1	5	102
42	Read, choose, use and record standard metric units to estimate and measure length, weight and capacity to a suitable degree of accuracy (eg the nearest centimetre); convert larger to smaller units using decimals to one place (eg change 2.6kg to 2600g).	(46) Units of measure	Refresh	1	6	103
42	Interpret a reading that lies between two unnumbered divisions on a scale.	(47) How much?	Read	1	8	104
43	Plan and pursue an enquiry; present evidence by collecting, organising and interpreting information; suggest extensions to the enquiry.	(48) Persuade me	Reason	1	10	106

Unit 2

	100 Mental Maths Starters			100 Maths Lessons		
Page	**Objective**	**Activity title**	**Starter type**	**Unit**	**Lesson**	**Page**
44	Read, choose, use and record standard metric units to estimate and measure length, weight and capacity to a suitable degree of accuracy (eg the nearest centimetre); convert larger to smaller units using decimals to one place (eg change 2.6kg to 2600g).	(49) Convert me!	Rehearse	2	1	113
45	Explain reasoning using diagrams, graphs and text; refine ways of recording using images and symbols.	(50) Match up	Refresh	2	5	116

Unit 2 ...continued

100 Mental Maths Starters				100 Maths Lessons		
Page	**Objective**	**Activity title**	**Starter type**	**Unit**	**Lesson**	**Page**
46	Read, choose, use and record standard metric units to estimate and measure length, weight and capacity to a suitable degree of accuracy (eg the nearest centimetre); convert larger to smaller units using decimals to one place (eg change 2.6kg to 2600g).	51 Containers	Reason	2	6	116
46	Interpret a reading that lies between two unnumbered divisions on a scale.	52 What a weight!	Read	2	7	117
47	Interpret a reading that lies between two unnumbered divisions on a scale.	53 Heat me up, cool me down!	Read	2	8	118
47	Describe the occurrence of familiar events using the language of chance or likelihood.	54 Surely not!	Rehearse	2	9	118

Unit 3

100 Mental Maths Starters				100 Maths Lessons		
Page	**Objective**	**Activity title**	**Starter type**	**Unit**	**Lesson**	**Page**
48	Read, choose, use and record standard metric units to estimate and measure length, weight and capacity to a suitable degree of accuracy (eg the nearest centimetre); convert larger to smaller units using decimals to one place (eg change 2.6kg to 2600g).	55 Measurement Bingo	Rehearse	3	2	125
49	Read, choose, use and record standard metric units to estimate and measure length, weight and capacity to a suitable degree of accuracy (eg the nearest centimetre); convert larger to smaller units using decimals to one place (eg change 2.6kg to 2600g).	56 Ordering mixed amounts	Recall	3	3	125
50	Describe the occurrence of familiar events using the language of chance or likelihood.	57 That's impossible!	Reason	3	5	127
50	Find and interpret the mode of a set of data.	58 All the rage	Rehearse	3	7	128
51	Read, choose, use and record standard metric units to estimate and measure length, weight and capacity to a suitable degree of accuracy (eg the nearest centimetre); convert larger to smaller units using decimals to one place (eg change 2.6kg to 2600g).	59 How much more?	Reason	3	9	129
51	Interpret a reading that lies between two unnumbered divisions on a scale.	60 Read me!	Refine	3	10	130

Maths in minutes

Resources
A board or flipchart; pencils and paper for each child

Learning objective
Extend mental methods for whole-number calculations.

Type of starter
Refresh

Mental strategy
Range of strategies: review in particular numbers that bridge 1000, multiplying by 10 and adjusting.

Answers

1. 88
2. 65
3. 84
4. 275
5. 375
6. 500
7. 23
8. 110
9. 1018

Write some questions on the board. Hide them and tell the class they will have three minutes to answer all of the questions. Provide sets covering different calculation types, for example:

Multiplying two-digit by one-digit numbers

1. 11 × 8
2. 13 × 5
3. 12 × 7

Multiplying by 25

4. 11 × 25
5. 15 × 25
6. 20 × 25

Subtracting one near multiple of 1000 from another

7. 2020 – 1997
8. 3080 – 2970
9. 4009 – 2991

Units of weight

Resources
A board or flipchart

Learning objective
Read, choose, use and record standard metric units to estimate and measure length, weight and capacity to a suitable degree of accuracy (eg the nearest centimetre); convert larger to smaller units using decimals to one place (eg change 2.6kg to 2600g).

Type of starter
Refresh

Mental strategy
Emphasise the relationship between kg and g, for example: 0.5kg = ½kg = 500g.

Answers

1. 500g
2. 250g
3. 750g
4. 1500g
5. 1250g
6. 1750g
7. 400g
8. 800g
9. 1800g
10. 2000g
11. 3000g
12. 5000g

Write '2.5kg = ____ g' on the board. Ask for the answer and methods used. Work through the questions below, converting from kilograms to grams.

1. ½kg
2. ¼kg
3. ¾kg
4. 1.5kg
5. 1.25kg
6. 1.75kg
7. 0.4kg
8. 0.8kg
9. 1.8kg
10. 2kg
11. 3kg
12. 5kg

45 Picture this!

Learning objective
Explain reasoning using diagrams, graphs and text; refine ways of recording using images and symbols.

Type of starter
Reason

Mental strategy
Remind the children that graphs and charts are a pictorial representation of data enabling the reader to see a lot of information at once.

- Bar graph/Bar line (stick): shows comparisons of different amounts, eg favourite foods/visitors each day.
- Line graph: shows continuous data over a period of time, eg heart rate/temperature.
- Pictogram: pictorial representation of data, especially useful if large numbers are involved. A key is needed to indicate this, eg one picture of a car represents 20 cars, therefore half a car represents 10 cars. It is less helpful for single numbers of items, unless used for young children.

Resources
A board or flipchart; types of graph (from photocopiable page 94) one per group; individual whiteboards and pens

Split the class into small groups. Write the following scenarios on the board.

1. The number of visitors to a library on each day of one week.
2. A comparison of the temperatures of London and Rome through each month of the year.
3. The numbers of different coloured cars in a car park.
4. The numbers of different electrical appliances in homes on a certain street.
5. Pulse rate from resting to during exercise.
6. A comparison of shoe sizes between boys and girls in our class.

Recap the different types of graph. Ask the children to look at the scenarios and to discuss which type of graph they would use to display each one.

Read out each scenario and ask the children to choose from the photocopiable sheet which type of graph they think is most appropriate. They should write the letter A, B, C or D on their whiteboards and hold them up to cast their vote, explaining their choice. Also ask them to say what they think would be represented on each axis.

Answers
1. A or C
2. B
3. A or D
4. D
5. B
6. A

46 Units of measure

Resources
A set of measures cards (metres, grams, kilometres, litres, millilitres, seconds, hours, minutes, kilograms, millimetres, centimetres) per pair or small group

Learning objective
Read, choose, use and record standard metric units to estimate and measure length, weight and capacity to a suitable degree of accuracy (eg the nearest centimetre); convert larger to smaller units using decimals to one place (eg change 2.6kg to 2600g).

Type of starter
Refresh

Distribute the measures cards and explain that the children must use them to vote for the most appropriate unit of measure to use for each item that you suggest. They should discuss their reasons before voting.

Suggest the most appropriate unit of measure for:

1. the height of a man
2. the weight of an egg
3. the length of the playground
4. the distance to Paris
5. the amount of juice in a carton
6. the amount of medicine in a bottle
7. the flying height of an aeroplane
8. the time taken to run 100m
9. the time taken to run a marathon
10. the time to eat a chocolate bar
11. the weight of a sack of potatoes
12. the length of your nails
13. the length of a pen.

Answers

1. metres
2. grams
3. metres
4. kilometres
5. litres
6. millilitres
7. kilometres or metres
8. seconds
9. hours
10. minutes
11. kilograms
12. millimetres
13. centimetres

47 How much?

Resources
Measuring containers/ scales containing different amounts, where the level falls between two numbered divisions on the scale, or the 'Measuring cylinder' and 'Measuring scales' ITPs and interactive whiteboard

Learning objective
Interpret a reading that lies between two unnumbered divisions on a scale.

Type of starter
Read

Mental strategy
Children may need to be helped in order to work out what each division on a scale is worth using the information that is numbered. For instance, if weighing scales are numbered in 100g amounts but there are four divisions (spaces not lines), the children should be able to divide 100 by 4 and work out that the unnumbered 'jumps' are worth 25g each.

No set answers

Ask the children to work through the amounts you have provided for them to measure, explaining to you as they go how they worked out the unnumbered amount, from the scale given.

48 Persuade me

Learning objective
Plan and pursue an enquiry; present evidence by collecting, organising and interpreting information; suggest extensions to the enquiry.

Type of starter
Reason

Resources
Paper for recording

Tell the children that in groups of three and four, they should imagine that they have to make a presentation to a panel of advertisers about the favourite chocolate bars of all the children in the class.

Their presentation should include a time plan to show how they would collect and present the information.

They must have a clear idea of how much time they would allocate to each part of the process, since they would have a maximum of one hour to complete it.

They must then present their ideas to the 'experts' (rest of the class) who will ask questions and decide on the suitability of the plan.

Plans should include:

- data collection (tally chart)
- a limited field, for example they should not ask 'What is your favourite chocolate bar?', rather 'Which of the following bars do you prefer?'
- time allocation for each task: 15 minutes for tally, 5 minutes to create a frequency table, 25 minutes to draw the graph and label it, and so on
- choice of a bar chart/bar line or pictogram, including a key
- clear understanding of what the graph shows and what each axis will represent
- idea of an appropriate scale for the axes.

No set answers

49 Convert me!

Resources
Individual whiteboards and pens

Learning objective
Read, choose, use and record standard metric units to estimate and measure length, weight and capacity to a suitable degree of accuracy (eg the nearest centimetre); convert larger to smaller units using decimals to one place (eg change 2.6kg to 2600g).

Type of starter
Rehearse

Answers
1. 1700m
2. 3500m
3. 3400g
4. 2.385kg
5. 90 min
6. 3.5l
7. 1900ml
8. 1000mm
9. 58mm
10. 0.98m

Ask the children a variety of equivalent measures conversion questions, which they should record in order to check their accuracy at the end.

1. How far in metres is 1.7 kilometres?
2. Write 3.5 kilometres as metres.
3. How many grams in 3.4 kilograms?
4. How much in kilograms is 2385 grams?
5. How many minutes is an hour and a half?
6. How many litres is 3500 millilitres?
7. Convert 1.9 litres to millilitres.
8. How many millimetres in 1 metre?
9. Write 5.8 centimetres in millimetres.
10. Write 98 centimetres as metres.

50 Match up

Learning objective
Explain reasoning using diagrams, graphs and text; refine ways of recording using images and symbols.

Type of starter
Refresh

Resources
The chart below copied onto a whiteboard or activity sheet

Ask the children to match the data type to the most appropriate graph or chart, giving their reasons.

A. Birthday months in our class	1. Bar graph/ Bar line graph
B. Visitors to 'Ocean World' centre over a year	2. Line graph
C. Different species of bird visiting our bird table	3. Venn diagram
D. Comparison of prices of sweets at different shops	4. Pictogram/Bar chart
E. Comparison of temperatures in three cities	5. Frequency chart/ Bar chart
F. My temperature over the 24 hours I was ill	6. Pictogram
G. Colours of cars that pass our school in a day	7. Comparison bar chart
H. Identifying common factors of two numbers	8. Line graph

Answers
A. 5
B. 1
C. 6
D. 7
E. 2 or 8
F. 2 or 8
G. 4
H. 3

51 Containers

Resources
A variety of measuring containers (eg measuring cylinder, various sizes and scales of cup, medicine spoons, bucket, jugs) or use the 'Measuring cylinder' ITP and change the maximum values; sticky notes or labels

Learning objective
Read, choose, use and record standard metric units to estimate and measure length, weight and capacity to a suitable degree of accuracy (eg the nearest centimetre); convert larger to smaller units using decimals to one place (eg change 2.6kg to 2600g).

Type of starter
Reason

No set answers

Examine the different scales on the containers available. Ask the children to identify the maximum value that each can measure and the marked divisions on the scale. Ask them to work out the values for any unmarked divisions. Record this information onto a sticky note and label each vessel.

Discuss what liquid amount might be measured using each container, for example the amount of juice in a cup, water to wash the car, medicine.

52 What a weight!

Resources
A variety of scales (eg bathroom scales, kitchen scales, balances, electronic scales, Newton meter) or 'Measuring scales' ITP, changing the scale as appropriate; sticky notes or labels

Learning objective
Interpret a reading that lies between two unnumbered divisions on a scale.

Type of starter
Read

No set answers

Examine the different scales on the weighing equipment available. Ask the children to identify the maximum value that each can measure and the marked divisions on the scale. Ask them to work out the values for any unmarked divisions. Record this information onto a sticky note and label each item.

Discuss what items might be measured using each piece of equipment, for example a man, an elephant, an egg, flour for a cake, a kitten.

Heat me up, cool me down!

Learning objective
Interpret a reading that lies between two unnumbered divisions on a scale.

Type of starter
Read

Resources
Thermometers; range of liquids/ items of different temperatures or 'Thermometer' ITP; recording equipment

Discuss as a class the divisions shown on the thermometer, including reading below zero.

Doing a circuit of the items you have provided, groups of children should measure the temperature of each item, giving an accurate reading, and record them for checking later. Ask them to explain their reasoning for any temperatures which lie between the marked divisions.

No set answers
Note that results may vary as the items cool down or warm up during the session

Surely not!

Learning objective
Describe the occurrence of familiar events using the language of chance or likelihood.

Type of starter
Rehearse

Resources
Pieces of card for each child to label as follows: Certain 1; Possible $\frac{3}{4}$; Even $\frac{1}{2}$; Unlikely $\frac{1}{4}$; Impossible 0

Establish what we mean by 'impossible' and 'certain' and all likelihoods in between, linked to their fraction equivalents. Describe how this is sometimes shown on a number line of likelihood.

Explain that you are going to say a number of events and that the children need to decide on the likelihood of these events occurring, along with an explanation of why they think this is the case. They must indicate their opinions by holding up the appropriate card.

Pose these scenarios:

1. We will have a fire drill today
2. There will be salad for school lunch
3. There will be extra homework this week
4. Chelsea will win this year's league
5. I shall teleport straight home tonight
6. Today, somewhere in the world the sun will shine

Invite the children to make up more examples of their own for each likelihood.

Answers
Answers will vary depending on your school:

1. unlikely
2. even
3. unlikely
4. possible
5. impossible
6. certain

55 Measurement Bingo

Resources
Individual whiteboards and pens; list of measures to choose from written up on a board or flipchart

Learning objective
Read, choose, use and record standard metric units to estimate and measure length, weight and capacity to a suitable degree of accuracy (eg the nearest centimetre); convert larger to smaller units using decimals to one place (eg change 2.6kg to 2600g).

Type of starter
Rehearse

Mental strategy
Know when the digits are going to become bigger or smaller, for example 2.3kg is multiplied by 1000 to become 2300g.

Understand that 340g is less than a thousand and therefore must be less than 1 kilogram, hence 0.340kg.

Explain to the children that they are going to play Bingo using equivalent measurements. Ask them to draw a 3 × 3 grid onto their whiteboards and to select one measure from the list provided to write into each box.

1. 1.5l
2. 750g
3. 0.45kg
4. 26cm
5. 2600g
6. 2490ml
7. 4900g
8. 85mm
9. 2300ml
10. 123cm
11. 397cm
12. 7000g
13. 34,000g
14. 2.3kg
15. 70km
16. 250g

Call out *Find the equivalent for...* and choose any of the equivalent amounts listed in the answers. Children must cross off the matching equivalents. The first person to cross out all of their equivalent measures is the winner.

Answers

1. 1.5l = 1500ml
2. 750g = 0.75kg
3. 0.45kg = 450g
4. 26cm = 260mm
5. 2600g = 2.6kg
6. 2490ml = 2.49l
7. 4900g = 4.9kg
8. 85mm = 8.5cm
9. 2300ml = 2.3l
10. 123cm = 1.23m
11. 397cm = 3.97m
12. 7000g = 7 kg
13. 34,000g = 34kg
14. 2.3kg = 2300g
15. 70km = 70,000m
16. 250g = 0.25kg

BLOCK C

56 Ordering mixed amounts

Learning objective
Read, choose, use and record standard metric units to estimate and measure length, weight and capacity to a suitable degree of accuracy (eg the nearest centimetre); convert larger to smaller units using decimals to one place (eg change 2.6kg to 2600g).

Type of starter
Recall

Mental strategy
It is important that the children are aware of mentally converting the measures to a common unit. Some will actually need to do this and jot them down before reordering.

Resources
A board or flipchart; individual whiteboards and pens

On the board, write up lists of mixed unit measures for weight, capacity and length.

Ask the children to reorder them, smallest first, explaining to you how they made their decisions when comparing equivalent and relative sizes.

1. 2500g, 2.6kg, 2.85kg, 2kg, 900g, 3kg
2. 3m, 80cm, 390cm, 3.85m, 3.95m, 350cm
3. 1m, 58cm, 165cm, 1500mm, 155cm, 1.6m
4. 1.9km, 22km, 2km, 2105m, 1950m
5. 2999m, 2567m, 1002m, 1.5m, 15m
6. 9.9m, 99cm, 999.9km, 99m, 99,000m

Answers

1. 900g, 2kg, 2500g, 2.6kg, 2.85kg, 3kg
2. 80cm, 3m, 350cm, 3.85m, 390cm, 3.95m
3. 58cm, 1m, 1500mm, 155cm, 1.6m, 165cm
4. 1.9km, 1950m, 2km, 2105m, 22km
5. 1.5m, 15m, 1002m, 2567m, 2999m
6. 99cm, 9.9m, 99m, 99,000m, 999.9km

57 That's impossible!

Resources
A board or flipchart; paper for recording; pencils; rulers; copy of the table headings on the board or an activity sheet

Learning objective
Describe the occurrence of familiar events using the language of chance or likelihood.

Type of starter
Reason

Mental strategy
Warn the children that their view may be affected by opinion. For example, Liverpool FC may be their favourite team but it is not absolutely certain that they will win every competition this year, since that is opinion and not fact.

No set answers

Certain (1)	Possible (¾ or 0.75)	Even chance (½ or 0.5)	Unlikely (¼ or 0.25)	Impossible (0)

Ask the children to discuss, in pairs, possible events that would fit into each likelihood category and to justify their ideas to the rest of the class.

58 All the rage

Resources
Individual whiteboards, or a large sheet of paper, and pens

Learning objective
Find and interpret the mode of a set of data.

Type of starter
Rehearse

Mental strategy
A simple frequency chart showing the data results. For example:

Our ages: the mode is 10

Sally	Tom	Ian	Ben	Amy	Sue
10	9	9	10	10	10

No set answers

Remind the children that the mode of a set of data means the most popular or most frequently occurring event. Tell them that you are going to make statements about the mode of a set of data. They must prove it by creating the data to match and then explain their reasoning. Diagrams or jottings may be drawn to show the possible data outcomes.

1. I threw a dice ten times. The mode was 4.
2. Out of our class of 30 people, the mode birthday month is June.
3. Out of 20 pet owners, the mode pet in our class is a cat.
4. Last month, my mode weekly mental maths score was 9 out of 10.
5. The mode weather was rain during the last week.
6. The mode age of my six friends is 10 years.

59 How much more?

Learning objective
Read, choose, use and record standard metric units to estimate and measure length, weight and capacity to a suitable degree of accuracy (eg the nearest centimetre); convert larger to smaller units using decimals to one place (eg change 2.6kg to 2600g).

Type of starter
Reason

Mental strategy
Children can count on in either units of grams or decimal fractions of a kilogram.

Resources
A board or flipchart; 'Measuring scales' ITP or a pair of weighing scales

Display the ITP or indicate the weighing scales. Ask the children to show you where 700g would be. Ask: *How much more flour would you need if a recipe requires 1kg of flour?*

Ask the children to work out the differences of the following weights by counting on.

1. 250g to 1.5kg
2. 2.6kg to 3000g
3. 450g to 1.2kg
4. 1.8kg to 2.5kg
5. 1.75kg to 2.6kg
6. 300g to 1.7kg
7. 4.5kg to 10kg
8. 3950g to 6.3kg
9. 120g to 2kg
10. 0.75kg to 3.1kg

Answers
1. 1.25kg/1250g
2. 0.4kg/400g
3. 0.75kg/750g
4. 0.7kg/700g
5. 0.85kg/850g
6. 1.4kg/1400g
7. 5.5kg/5500g
8. 2.35kg/2350g
9. 1880g/1.88kg
10. 2.35kg/2350g

60 Read me!

Learning objective
Interpret a reading that lies between two unnumbered divisions on a scale.

Type of starter
Refine

Mental strategy
Encourage the children to look at the number of main divisions to the maximum value. For instance, if there are ten main divisions it is likely that the maximum value will be a multiple of ten. Similarly, with the smaller divisions, four is likely to represent a multiple of four such as 4 × 25g.

Resources
'Measuring cylinder' ITP and 'Measuring scales' ITP or drawings of empty scales on which the numbers have been removed leaving only the divisions

Using the measuring cylinder ITP, blank the scale and ask the children to tell you the maximum capacity of the measuring cylinder and what each division might be worth. Then partially fill the cylinder and ask them to read the amount in both millilitres and litres. Repeat with weight on the 'Measuring scales' ITP. Change the blank scale several times and repeat the activity, ensuring that the children are able to explain how they worked out the values.

No set answers

BLOCK D

Unit 1

100 Mental Maths Starters				100 Maths Lessons		
Page	Objective	Activity title	Starter type	Unit	Lesson	Page
54	Solve one-step and two-step problems involving whole numbers and decimals and all four operations, choosing and using appropriate calculation strategies, including calculator use.	61 Word problems	Reason	1	1	137
55	Read timetables and time using 24-hour clock notation; use a calendar to calculate time intervals.	62 Show me	Rehearse	1	3	139
56	Solve one-step and two-step problems involving whole numbers and decimals and all four operations, choosing and using appropriate calculation strategies, including calculator use.	63 Pairs to 1000	Rehearse	1	4	140
56	Interpret a reading that lies between two unnumbered divisions on a scale.	64 More measures	Read	1	6	141
57	Read and plot coordinates in the first quadrant; recognise parallel and perpendicular lines in grids and shapes; use a set-square and ruler to draw shapes with perpendicular or parallel sides.	65 Shape coordinates	Refresh	1	8	142
57	Read, choose, use and record standard metric units to estimate and measure length, weight and capacity to a suitable degree of accuracy (eg the nearest centimetre); convert larger to smaller units using decimals to one place (eg change 2.6kg to 2600g).	66 How long?	Refresh	1	10	144

Unit 2

100 Mental Maths Starters				100 Maths Lessons		
Page	Objective	Activity title	Starter type	Unit	Lesson	Page
58	Draw and measure lines to the nearest millimetre; measure and calculate the perimeter of regular and irregular polygons; use the formula for the area of a rectangle to calculate a rectangle's area.	67 Area estimates	Rehearse	2	1	150
58	Use knowledge of rounding, place value, number facts and inverse operations to estimate and check calculations.	68 Area problems	Refine	2	2	150
59	Solve one-step and two-step problems involving whole numbers and decimals and all four operations, choosing and using appropriate calculation strategies, including calculator use.	69 Playground area	Reason	2	5	153

Unit 2 ...continued

100 Mental Maths Starters				100 Maths Lessons		
Page	Objective	Activity title	Starter type	Unit	Lesson	Page
59	Use knowledge and understanding of place value to multiply and divide whole numbers and decimals by 10, 100 or 1000.	70 Beat 10,000	Refresh	2	6	154
60	Read, choose, use and record standard metric units to estimate and measure length, weight and capacity to a suitable degree of accuracy (eg the nearest centimetre); convert larger to smaller units using decimals to one place (eg change 2.6kg to 2600g).	71 Quick-fire measures	Rehearse	2	8	156
60	Measure and calculate the perimeter of regular and irregular polygons; use the formula for the area of a rectangle to calculate the rectangle's area.	72 Perimeter and area	Rehearse	2	9	156

Unit 3

100 Mental Maths Starters				100 Maths Lessons		
Page	Objective	Activity title	Starter type	Unit	Lesson	Page
61	Read timetables and time using 24-hour clock notation; use a calendar to calculate time intervals.	73 Clock faces	Recall	3	1	161
62	Read timetables and time using 24-hour clock notation; use a calendar to calculate time intervals.	74 Blind date	Rehearse	3	4	163
63	Read, choose, use and record standard metric units to estimate and measure length, weight and capacity to a suitable degree of accuracy (eg the nearest centimetre); convert larger to smaller units using decimals to one place (eg change 2.6kg to 2600g).	75 Share out	Refine	3	6	165
64	Read, choose, use and record standard metric units to estimate and measure length, weight and capacity to a suitable degree of accuracy (eg the nearest centimetre); convert larger to smaller units using decimals to one place (eg change 2.6kg to 2600g).	76 Quantity confusion	Refresh	3	7	166
65	Draw and measure lines to the nearest millimetre; measure and calculate the perimeter of regular and irregular polygons; use the formula for the area of a rectangle to calculate a rectangle's area.	77 Estimating areas	Reason	3	9	167
65	Draw and measure lines to the nearest millimetre; measure and calculate the perimeter of regular and irregular polygons; use the formula for the area of a rectangle to calculate a rectangle's area.	78 Finding areas	Rehearse	3	10	168

BLOCK D

61 Word problems

Resources
Individual whiteboards and pens

Learning objective
Solve one-step and two-step problems involving whole numbers and decimals and all four operations, choosing and using appropriate calculation strategies, including calculator use.

Type of starter
Reason

Mental strategy
Discuss the methods used to solve some of the problems.

Children should raise a hand to answer or write answers on their individual whiteboards to show you.

1. Three apples cost 6p each. How much is that altogether?
2. I cut a 26cm piece of string in half. How long was each piece?
3. How much more do I need to be able to buy a £5 CD if I have £4.93?
4. A square has an area of $9cm^2$. How long is each side?
5. When I add 6 to this number, the answer is half of 30.
6. I was given 33p change from 50p. How much had I spent?
7. We bought six two-litre bottles of lemonade ready for the barbecue. How many litres was that?
8. The bag that I bought had been reduced by £3 from £9. How much did I pay?
9. We shared 28 cards equally between the two of us. How many each did we have?
10. If I add 0.1 to 0.9, what is the answer?
11. What is the area of a rectangle that measures 5cm by 3cm?
12. The perimeter of a rectangle is 24cm. Its width is 4cm. What is its length?
13. If I add 1 to my mystery number, I will have one quarter of 80. What is my number?
14. I weighed 250g of flour into each bowl to empty my 1kg bag. How many bowls did I need?
15. If I add 89 to my number, I make 100. What is my number?

Answers

1. 18p
2. 13cm
3. 7p
4. 3cm
5. 9
6. 17p
7. 12 litres
8. £6
9. 14
10. 1 (or 1.0)
11. $15cm^2$
12. 8cm
13. 19
14. 4
15. 11

Show me

Learning objective
Read timetables and time using 24-hour clock notation; use a calendar to calculate time intervals.

Type of starter
Rehearse

Resources
A card clock face for each child

Children should raise a hand to respond, then show the answer on their clock face (or give verbal responses where appropriate).

1. I should be in school by 8.45am, but I am 10 minutes late. What time is it?
2. My favourite TV programme starts at 19.10. Show this time.
3. The programme lasts for half an hour from 19.10. At what time does it finish?
4. Show the time 20 minutes after 15.45. How else could we say this time?
5. The film starts at 18.30. I am meeting my friends quarter of an hour before. When is that?
6. The train arrived at 11.30 after a journey of 1 hour 20 minutes. At what time did it leave?
7. Show me 6.47am. What would that be in 24-hour time?
8. Tell me another way to say 6.47.
9. Show me 2.38pm. What would this time be in 24-hour time?
10. How else can we say 2.38?
11. The video lasts for 1 hour 45 minutes. It started at 5.15pm. At what time will it finish?
12. My watch is showing 6.10, but it is now 6.50. For how long has it been stopped?
13. Show me the time 45 minutes after 2.20.
14. Show me the time 25 minutes before 10.45.
15. A PE starter activity lasted for 35 minutes. If it ended at 2.55pm, at what time did it start?

Answers

1. 8.55am
2. 7.10
3. 19:40
4. 4.05; 5 past 4
5. 18.15
6. 10.10
7. 06.47
8. 13 minutes to 7
9. 14.38
10. 22 minutes to 3
11. 7pm
12. 40 minutes
13. 3.05
14. 10.20
15. 2.20

63 Pairs to 1000

Resources
A set of numeral cards 0–9 (from photocopiable page 89) for each group

Learning objective
Solve one-step and two-step problems involving whole numbers and decimals and all four operations, choosing and using appropriate calculation strategies, including calculator use.

Type of starter
Rehearse

Answers

1.	150	9.	600
2.	250	10.	900
3.	450	11.	300
4.	750	12.	700
5.	950	13.	400
6.	850	14.	800
7.	350	15.	100
8.	650	16.	500

Organise the children in mixed-ability groups of three, standing up.

Tell the children that when they have worked out 'how many more to 1000' from the given number, they must hold up numeral cards (one card per child) in the correct order to show the answer.

1. 850	2. 750	3. 550	4. 250
5. 50	6. 150	7. 650	8. 350

Discuss the strategies used and the pattern of their answers.

For the next set of questions each group should say, all together, the other number of the pair to make 1000.

9. 400	10. 100	11. 700	12. 300
13. 600	14. 200	15. 900	16. 500

64 More measures

Resources
Individual whiteboards and pens; measuring equipment: metre sticks, trundle wheels, tape measures; different sized balls/beanbags

Learning objective
Interpret a reading that lies between two unnumbered divisions on a scale.

Type of starter
Read

Mental strategy
Discuss with the children their choice of measuring equipment to maximise accuracy. Ask: *How accurate is a trundle wheel?*

No set answers

Organise the children into groups of three or four. Explain that they are going to investigate which ball/beanbag is easiest to throw the furthest. Discuss safety issues, for example not walking in front of the throwing area.

Ensure that the children have a marker to indicate their starting throwing point. Ask them to choose their own throwing technique for maximum distance. The rest of the group are responsible for choosing the most appropriate equipment to accurately measure and record each throw.

65 Shape coordinates

Learning objective
Read and plot coordinates in the first quadrant; recognise parallel and perpendicular lines in grids and shapes; use a set-square and ruler to draw shapes with perpendicular or parallel sides.

Type of starter
Refresh

Mental strategy
It is important that coordinates are given in the correct order (x, y). That is, the horizontal axis first, followed by the vertical axis. Tell the children that a way to remember this is that they 'go along the corridor, then up the stairs'.

Resources
Labelled 15 × 15 coordinate grid, either on an interactive whiteboard, OHP or large squared paper; coloured pens

Demonstrate some points on the grid and ask the children to name the coordinates. Ask for a volunteer to mark some shape coordinates on the grid. Before they mark the final coordinate of each shape, ask the rest of the class: *What shape do you think is being made by the coordinates? What could the missing coordinate be?*

(2, 1), (3, 3), (4, 1) gives an equilateral triangle.

(5, 2), (4, 4), (2, 4), (3, 2) gives a parallelogram.

Repeat with other shape coordinates.

No set answers

66 How long?

Learning objective
Read, choose, use and record standard metric units to estimate and measure length, weight and capacity to a suitable degree of accuracy (eg the nearest centimetre); convert larger to smaller units using decimals to one place (eg change 2.6kg to 2600g).

Type of starter
Refresh

Mental strategy
Tell the children that estimating is easier if they have a known measure to compare with. For instance, if their height is approximately 1.5m this helps in estimating other lengths. Begin by estimating and measuring as a whole class to model the comparison technique and check accuracy. Later, small groups could continue to work independently.

Resources
A board or flipchart for recording; a variety of measuring equipment (rulers, tape measure, metre stick); items to measure

Draw a table with three columns onto the board. Write the headings: 'Item', 'Estimate', 'Actual measure'. Select everyday items from around school. For each item, ask the children to estimate the length. Then, ask for a volunteer to measure the length. Record the measurements in the table.

No set answers

Area estimates

Resources
A board or flipchart on which you have drawn a variety of different-sized rectangles labelled 'A', 'B', 'C' etc (or use an interactive whiteboard but not showing squared grid behind it); individual whiteboards and pens

Learning objective
Draw and measure lines to the nearest millimetre; measure and calculate the perimeter of regular and irregular polygons; use the formula for the area of a rectangle to calculate a rectangle's area.

Type of starter
Rehearse

Mental strategy
Discuss what is meant by area and the formula for working it out: area of a rectangle is calculated by length × breadth.

No set answers

Indicate the different rectangles and ask the children to estimate which has the biggest area. Ask them to rank the rectangles by letter on their whiteboards, largest to smallest.

Ask for volunteers to come and measure each rectangle in centimetres. Ask the class to work out the area and to write it on their whiteboards in order to show you. Check whose estimates were the most accurate.

Area problems

Resources
A board or flipchart; paper for drawing; rulers; pencils

Learning objective
Use knowledge of rounding, place value, number facts and inverse operations to estimate and check calculations.

Type of starter
Refine

Mental strategy
Some children will find the place value of multiplying decimals very difficult and may need to use a formal written calculation.

No set answers

Ask the children to draw a rectangle, as accurately as they can with the dimensions 6.5cm × 3cm.

Ask: *How would you multiply a decimal by partitioning? Now use that to work out the area of the rectangle.* (19.5cm^2)

Now ask them to draw a rectangle 3.2cm × 4.1cm. Discuss how jottings may be needed to find the area of this shape. (13.12cm^2)

Ask them to draw two more rectangles and to find their area.

4.5cm × 5cm (22.5cm^2)

5.1cm × 6cm (30.6cm^2)

Playground area

Learning objective
Solve one-step and two-step problems involving whole numbers and decimals and all four operations, choosing and using appropriate calculation strategies, including calculator use.

Type of starter
Reason

Resources
Individual whiteboards or paper and pencils; calculators

Ask the class to design a sandpit area for a group of young children. It must have an area of 36m^2. Ask them to draw to scale (using the key: 1cm = 1m) the various possible rectangular shapes that it might be. (Some children might even think of composite 'L' shapes.)

Next, ask them to discuss with a partner the shape that would give the children the best space to play and reasons why. (Generally, a squarer shape would give optimum playing area.)

Answers
1. 1m × 36m
2. 2m × 18m
3. 3m × 12m
4. 4m × 9m
5. 6m × 6m

Beat 10,000

Learning objective
Use knowledge and understanding of place value to multiply and divide whole numbers and decimals by 10, 100 or 1000.

Type of starter
Refresh

Mental strategy
Reinforce the strategy of moving digits up and down in place value in order to multiply or divide by 10 and 100. For children who are less confident, a calculator may be used in order to reinforce the moving place value.

Resources
Individual whiteboards or paper and pencils; numeral cards 0–9 (from photocopiable page 89) one set per group; counters (labelled '×10', '×100', '÷10', '÷100' and hidden in a bag or box) one set per group; calculators

Organise the children into groups of four or five. Using the numeral cards, each group generates a two-digit number. Player 1 writes this number on his/her whiteboard, picks an instruction counter at random and applies the operation to the number on their whiteboard. They replace the instruction counter. Player 2 writes player 1's total on his/her whiteboard, picks an instruction counter and applies the operation to the number on their whiteboard (player 1's total), and so on.

The player to reach 10,000 or more gains a point and generates a new two-digit number.

A recording card might look like this:

TTh	Th	H	T	U	.	t	h	th	
			2	4	.				(Original number: 24)
		2	4	0	.				(Operation: '×10')
				2	.	4			(Operation: '÷100')
		2	4	0	.				(Operation: '×100')
2	4	0	0	0	.				(Operation: '×100' = WINNER)

No set answers

71 Quick-fire measures

Resources
Individual whiteboards and pens

Learning objective
Read, choose, use and record standard metric units to estimate and measure length, weight and capacity to a suitable degree of accuracy (eg the nearest centimetre); convert larger to smaller units using decimals to one place (eg change 2.6kg to 2600g).

Type of starter
Rehearse

Mental strategy
Revise the calculation of multiplying and dividing by 1000 to convert kilograms to grams. Anything less than 1000 is not a whole kilogram.

Answers

1. 2300g
2. 4400g
3. 2750g
4. 12,200g
5. 6850g
6. 9995g
7. 270g
8. 3230g
9. 194,500g
10. 670g

Ask the children to do some quick-fire equivalent conversions of the measures that you call out. They should write the answer on their whiteboards and turn them around when you say *Show me*.

Choose one or other of these questions or answers and ask the children to write down the equivalent:

1. 2.3kg
2. 4.4kg
3. 2.75kg
4. 12.2kg
5. 6.85kg
6. 9.995kg
7. 0.27kg
8. 3.23kg
9. 19.45kg
10. 0.67kg

72 Perimeter and area

Resources
A board or flipchart; individual whiteboards and pens

Learning objective
Measure and calculate the perimeter of regular and irregular polygons; use the formula for the area of a rectangle to calculate the rectangle's area.

Type of starter
Rehearse

Mental strategy
Remind children:

- the area of a rectangle is its width times its height
- the perimeter of a rectangle is its distance around, or two times its height plus two times its width.

Answers

1. Area: 24, Perimeter: 20
2. Area: 27, Perimeter: 24

Draw some rectangles on the board with the following dimensions labelled:

1. width 6, height 4
2. width 9, height 3

Ask the children to write the perimeter and area of each rectangle. Increase the difficulty level in subsequent sessions.

73 Clock faces

Learning objective
Read timetables and time using 24-hour clock notation; use a calendar to calculate time intervals.

Type of starter
Recall

Resources
A board or flipchart; a clock card for each child

Write 16.20 on the board. Ask for the 12-hour clock time. Stress that because 16 comes after 12, it is afternoon. Count on from 12 to 16 to show that 16.00 is the same as 4.00pm. So 16.20 is the same as 4.20pm.

Ask the children to show these times as 12-hour clock times. Emphasise that because they are all afternoon times, 'pm' will be needed.

1. 17.00
2. 20.00
3. 20.15
4. 20.50
5. 14.30
6. 18.55
7. 23.20
8. 21.05
9. 13.35
10. 19.10
11. 15.40
12. 22.25
13. 16.45
14. 23.55
15. 14.00

Answers

1. 5.00pm
2. 8.00pm
3. 8.15pm
4. 8.50pm
5. 2.30pm
6. 6.55pm
7. 11.20pm
8. 9.05pm
9. 1.35pm
10. 7.10pm
11. 3.40pm
12. 10.25pm
13. 4.45pm
14. 11.55pm
15. 2.00pm

74 Blind date

Resources
A board or flipchart

Learning objective
Read timetables and time using 24-hour clock notation; use a calendar to calculate time intervals.

Type of starter
Rehearse

Mental strategy
Essential information for solving this type of question is knowledge of how many days there are in each month.

You could teach the old rhyme:

30 days has September, April, June and November, all the rest have 31, except February, which has 28 clear and 29 each Leap Year.

Also help the children to count on and back in days starting from the NEXT day rather than the one they are currently on.

Answers
1. Monday 7 September
2. Monday 24 August
3. Saturday 26 September
4. Wednesday 14 October
5. Friday

Copy this fragment of a calendar onto the board:

September						
Sun	Mon	Tues	Wed	Thurs	Fri	Sat
		1	2	3	4	5
6	7	8	9	10	11	
13	14	15	16	17		
20	21	22	23			
27	28	29				

Explain to the children that part of the calendar is missing and they need to use what is there to answer some questions.

1. We returned to school on the first Monday in September. What was the date?
2. Jane's birthday was eight days before the beginning of September. What was the day and date?
3. What date was the last Saturday in September?
4. Angie's birthday is two weeks into the next month. What is the day and date?
5. Calculate what day of the week Christmas day (25th December) will be in this calendar year.

75 Share out

Learning objective
Read, choose, use and record standard metric units to estimate and measure length, weight and capacity to a suitable degree of accuracy (eg the nearest centimetre); convert larger to smaller units using decimals to one place (eg change 2.6kg to 2600g).

Type of starter
Refine

Resources
A board or flipchart; individual whiteboards or paper and pencils for recording

Write the questions on the board. Explain that the children must work in pairs to solve problems involving multiplying and dividing measures in real-life situations.

1. Here is a recipe for making soup. It serves four people.

   120g onions
   2 sticks of celery
   80g tomatoes
   150g potatoes
   1 leek
   100g carrots
   10g mixed dried herbs
   500ml of vegetable stock
   50g pearl barley

Adjust the recipe to make enough soup for:

   a) two people

   b) 16 people.

2. I used 3.25 litres of paint to cover five walls. How much paint do I need to coat just one?

3. I have a journey to my holiday cottage of 1246km. I want to split it into roughly three equal 'legs'. How far will I travel each day?

4. If I need 75g of cherries for one cake, how many do I need to make six cakes?

5. It takes 20ml of squash to make one glass. How many glasses can I make from a 1 litre bottle?

Answers

1. a) 60g onions, 1 stick celery, 40g tomatoes, 75g potatoes, ½ a leek, 50g carrots, 5g herbs, 250ml stock, 25g pearl barley

   b) 480g onions, 8 sticks celery, 320g tomatoes, 600g potatoes, 4 leeks, 400g carrots, 40g herbs, 2 litres stock, 200g pearl barley

2. 0.65 litres or 650ml

3. Approximately 415km, 415km and 416km

4. 450g

5. 50

76 Quantity confusion

Resources
Individual whiteboards or paper and pencils for recording

Learning objective
Read, choose, use and record standard metric units to estimate and measure length, weight and capacity to a suitable degree of accuracy (eg the nearest centimetre); convert larger to smaller units using decimals to one place (eg change 2.6kg to 2600g).

Type of starter
Refresh

Mental strategy
Convert all the measurements to one common unit before adding.

Ask the children to rewrite the following statements so that all measures are in the same units and then calculate them.

1. For a cake I need 250g plain flour, 0.455kg self raising flour and 1kg and 200g of rice flour. How much is that altogether?
2. A fruit punch contains 1.5 litres of apple juice, 550ml pineapple juice, 0.03 litres of lemon juice and 1 litre and 400ml of strawberry juice. How much punch will I make altogether?
3. I walk 850m to Sally's house, 1km and 50m to Jane's house and 1287m to Will's house. How far have I travelled?
4. The pool attendant adds 1345 litres of hot water, 1783 litres of cold water and 0.030 litres of chemicals. How much liquid is in there altogether?
5. In my project, 1m 55cm of paper is covered with maps, 2.98m with illustrations and 589cm with writing. How long is my entire project?

Answers

1. 1905g or 1.905kg
2. 3480ml or 3.48 litres
3. 3.187km or 3187m
4. 3128.03 litres
5. 1042cm or 10.42m

77 Estimating areas

Learning objective
Draw and measure lines to the nearest millimetre; measure and calculate the perimeter of regular and irregular polygons; use the formula for the area of a rectangle to calculate a rectangle's area.

Type of starter
Reason

Mental strategy
Children will need to estimate in centimetres or metres for this activity. Guide them to use a benchmark measure, such as their hand span or their height, to achieve reasonably accurate estimates. Remind them to round their estimate, since a ½ metre is a reasonable margin of error. Remind them that the length × breadth measurement only works for rectangular shapes, so they may need to 'square off' any unusual shapes or, in the case of an 'L' shaped playground, work out two composite shapes.

Resources
Individual whiteboards and pens; rectangular objects from around the school

Hold up two different-sized books. Ask the children to estimate the approximate area of each. Ask them how they did it. Talk about rounding and estimating. Ask them to estimate the areas of common objects in and around school, for example:

- the classroom floor
- a window
- the playground
- books or newspapers
- the table top
- a piece of paper
- an envelope.

They must choose the correct unit of measurement and record their estimates. Compare their estimates and discuss the variation.

No set answers

78 Finding areas

Learning objective
Draw and measure lines to the nearest millimetre; measure and calculate the perimeter of regular and irregular polygons; use the formula for the area of a rectangle to calculate a rectangle's area.

Type of starter
Rehearse

Mental strategy
Revise how to use measuring equipment accurately, especially rulers or tape measures that have a 'dead space' at the beginning. Ensure that they always measure from zero.

Resources
A board or flipchart; individual whiteboards or paper and pencils; rectangular objects from around the school; measuring equipment: rulers, tape measures, metre sticks

Explain to the children that they are going to measure, as accurately as they can, various common rectangular objects and then calculate their areas. If they have previously estimated areas, they could use their measurements to check their estimates.

No set answers

BLOCK E

Unit 1

100 Mental Maths Starters				100 Maths Lessons		
Page	Objective	Activity title	Starter type	Unit	Lesson	Page
68	Recall quickly multiplication facts up to 10 × 10 and use them to multiply pairs of multiples of 10 and 100; derive quickly corresponding division facts.	79 Quick division	Recall	1	1	174
69	Extend mental methods for whole-number calculations, for example to multiply a two-digit number by a one-digit number (eg 12 × 9), to multiply by 25 (eg 16 × 25), to subtract one near-multiple of 1000 from another (eg 6070 – 4097).	80 Place value	Refresh	1	5	176
69	Find fractions using division (eg $^1/_{100}$ of 5kg), and percentages of numbers and quantities (eg 10%, 5% and 15% of £80).	81 Fractions of shapes	Refresh	1	6	177
70	Identify pairs of factors of two-digit whole numbers and find common multiples (eg for 6 and 9).	82 Factor pairs	Recall	1	7	178
70	Recall quickly multiplication facts up to 10 × 10 and use them to multiply pairs of multiples of 10 and 100; derive quickly corresponding division facts.	83 Square roots	Refresh	1	8	178
71	Recall quickly multiplication facts up to 10 × 10 and use them to multiply pairs of multiples of 10 and 100; derive quickly corresponding division facts.	84 Ordering multiples	Recall	1	9	179
72	Find fractions using division (eg $^1/_{100}$ of 5kg), and percentages of numbers and quantities (eg 10%, 5% and 15% of £80).	85 Finding percentages	Reason	1	10	180
72	Express a smaller whole number as a fraction of a larger one (eg recognise that 5 out of 8 is $^5/_8$); find equivalent fractions (eg $^7/_{10} = {}^{14}/_{20}$, or $^{19}/_{10} = 1^9/_{10}$); relate fractions to their decimal representations.	86 Fraction match	Refine	1	14	183

Unit 2

100 Mental Maths Starters				100 Maths Lessons		
Page	Objective	Activity title	Starter type	Unit	Lesson	Page
73	Find fractions using division (eg $^1/_{100}$ of 5kg), and percentages of numbers and quantities (eg 10%, 5% and 15% of £80).	87 Numeral cards	Recall	2	1	190
74	Express a smaller whole number as a fraction of a larger one (eg recognise that 5 out of 8 is $^5/_8$); find equivalent fractions (eg $^7/_{10} = {}^{14}/_{20}$, or $^{19}/_{10} = 1^9/_{10}$); relate fractions to their decimal representations.	88 Fractions Bingo	Rehearse	2	3	191
74	Understand percentage as the number of parts in every 100 and express tenths and hundredths as percentages.	89 Percentage families	Rehearse	2	5	192

Unit 2 ...continued

100 Mental Maths Starters				100 Maths Lessons		
Page	Objective	Activity title	Starter type	Unit	Lesson	Page
75	Use knowledge of place value and addition and subtraction of two-digit numbers to derive sums and differences and doubles and halves of decimals (eg 6.5 ± 2.7, half of 5.6, double 0.34).	(90) Doubling decimals chain	Refine	2	6	193
75	Use knowledge of place value and addition and subtraction of two-digit numbers to derive sums and differences and doubles and halves of decimals (eg 6.5 ± 2.7, half of 5.6, double 0.34).	(91) Decimals to make 10	Rehearse	2	8	194
76	Use knowledge of place value and addition and subtraction of two-digit numbers to derive sums and differences and doubles and halves of decimals (eg 6.5 ± 2.7, half of 5.6, double 0.34).	(92) Totally decimal	Refine	2	10	195
76	Use knowledge of place value and addition and subtraction of two-digit numbers to derive sums and differences and doubles and halves of decimals (eg 6.5 ± 2.7, half of 5.6, double 0.34).	(93) Decimal differences	Refine	2	11	196
77	Find fractions using division (eg $^{1}/_{100}$ of 5kg), and percentages of numbers and quantities (eg 10%, 5% and 15% of £80).	(94) Trios	Rehearse	2	14	198

Unit 3

100 Mental Maths Starters				100 Maths Lessons		
Page	Objective	Activity title	Starter type	Unit	Lesson	Page
78	Express a smaller whole number as a fraction of a larger one (eg recognise that 5 out of 8 is $^{5}/_{8}$); find equivalent fractions (eg $^{7}/_{10}$ = $^{14}/_{20}$, or $^{19}/_{10}$ = $1^{9}/_{10}$); relate fractions to their decimal representations.	(95) Matching on a number line	Refine	3	3	206
79	Express a smaller whole number as a fraction of a larger one (eg recognise that 5 out of 8 is $^{5}/_{8}$); find equivalent fractions (eg $^{7}/_{10}$ = $^{14}/_{20}$, or $^{19}/_{10}$ = $1^{9}/_{10}$); relate fractions to their decimal representations.	(96) Fractions and percentages	Refresh	3	5	209
80	Find fractions using division (eg $^{1}/_{100}$ of 5kg), and percentages of numbers and quantities (eg 10%, 5% and 15% of £80).	(97) Fractions of numbers	Rehearse	3	6	209
81	Solve one-step and two-step problems involving whole numbers and decimals and all four operations, choosing and using appropriate calculation strategies, including calculator use.	(98) Fraction problems	Reason	3	7	210
82	Find fractions using division (eg $^{1}/_{100}$ of 5kg), and percentages of numbers and quantities (eg 10%, 5% and 15% of £80).	(99) Quick-fire percentages	Rehearse	3	9	212
83	Express a smaller whole number as a fraction of a larger one (eg recognise that 5 out of 8 is $^{5}/_{8}$); find equivalent fractions (eg $^{7}/_{10}$ = $^{14}/_{20}$, or $^{19}/_{10}$ = $1^{9}/_{10}$); relate fractions to their decimal representations.	(100) Fraction number line	Rehearse	3	11	213
84	Represent a puzzle or problem by identifying and recording the information or calculations needed to solve it; find possible solutions and confirm them in the context of the problem.	(101) The bigger share	Reason	3	13	214
85	Use sequences to scale numbers up or down; solve problems involving proportions of quantities (eg decrease quantities in a recipe designed to feed six people).	(102) What's for tea?	Reason	3	15	215

79 Quick division

Resources
Numeral cards 1-10 (from photocopiable page 89) one set per child

Learning objective
Recall quickly multiplication facts up to 10 × 10 and use them to multiply pairs of multiples of 10 and 100; derive quickly corresponding division facts.

Type of starter
Recall

This is a rapid recall test. The children should spread out the numeral cards on their tables. Read out each question, pause, then give a silent signal (eg a raised hand) for the children to respond by holding up a numeral card.

1. 20 divided by 5
2. How many 3s make 18?
3. Divide 48 by 6
4. What is the quotient of 40 and 10?
5. Halve 18
6. How many 9s in 54?
7. 40 divided by 4
8. How many times can 4 be taken from 12?
9. Divide 49 by 7
10. Share 30 by 6
11. Find a quarter of 28
12. 32 divided by 8
13. 12 divided by 2
14. How many 7s in 21?
15. Divide 36 by 9
16. Divide 80 by 10
17. Half of 14 is...?
18. What is the quotient of 27 and 3?
19. How many 8s in 56?
20. How many times can 5 be taken from 40?
21. 63 divided by 7
22. 15 divided by 3
23. Divide 42 by 6
24. What is the quotient of 40 and 8?
25. How many 9s make 81?
26. How many 10s make 100?
27. 16 divided by 8
28. 6 divided by 2
29. Share 50 by 5
30. Divide 24 by 4

Answers

1. 4
2. 6
3. 8
4. 4
5. 9
6. 6
7. 10
8. 3
9. 7
10. 5
11. 7
12. 4
13. 6
14. 3
15. 4
16. 8
17. 7
18. 9
19. 7
20. 8
21. 9
22. 5
23. 7
24. 5
25. 9
26. 10
27. 2
28. 3
29. 10
30. 6

80 Place value

Learning objective
Extend mental methods for whole-number calculations, for example to multiply a two-digit number by a one-digit number (eg 12 × 9), to multiply by 25 (eg 16 × 25), to subtract one near-multiple of 1000 from another (eg 6070 - 4097).

Type of starter
Refresh

Mental strategy
Remind the children of the rule that the digits in these calculations always remain the same but move up and down the place value, with zeros holding the place value as necessary.

Resources
A board or flipchart; individual whiteboards and pens

Write the following calculations on the board and ask the children to jot down their answers. Check their accuracy and understanding of place value.

1. 34 × 10
2. 2.8 × 100
3. 76 ÷ 100
4. 420 ÷ 100
5. 321 ÷ 10
6. 21 × 100
7. 784 ÷ 10
8. 95 × 100
9. 31 × 100
10. 8.4 ÷ 10

Answers

1. 340
2. 280
3. 0.76
4. 4.2
5. 32.1
6. 2100
7. 78.4
8. 9500
9. 3100
10. 0.84

81 Fractions of shapes

Learning objective
Find fractions using division (eg $^1/_{100}$ of 5kg), and percentages of numbers and quantities (eg 10%, 5% and 15% of £80).

Type of starter
Refresh

Mental strategy
Remind the children that fractions are equal divisions of an object or number. Discuss how some shapes are easier to divide equally than others. Ensure that they understand that ¼ is one piece out of the possible four the shape was divided into. Revise the language of fractions, such as: numerator (the top number; the number of pieces shaded), denominator (bottom number; total number of pieces there are) and fraction names (one quarter, not one fourth).

Resources
A board or flipchart; large squared paper or 'Area' ITP

Draw a variety of shapes: squares, rectangles, circles and hexagons. On the square, shade in ¼ and ask the class to identify the fraction shaded. Repeat for other shapes and different fractions, asking for volunteers to come and shade the shape appropriately.

No set answers

82 Factor pairs

Resources
A board or flipchart; a set of numeral cards 0–10 (from photocopiable page 89) for each child

Learning objective
Identify pairs of factors of two-digit whole numbers and find common multiples (eg for 6 and 9).

Type of starter
Recall

Mental strategy
Ask the children for two numbers that, when multiplied together, will make 8. Remind them that 1, 2, 4 and 8 are factors of 8. Discuss the answers to the questions. Encourage the children to see that different multiplication facts can have the same answer (eg 4 × 3 and 2 × 6).

Answers
1. 2, 5 or 1, 10
2. 3, 4 or 2, 6
3. 2, 9 or 3, 6
4. 3, 2 or 6, 1
5. 6, 4 or 8, 3
6. 4, 5 or 2, 10
7. 8, 2 or 4, 4
8. no factors

Ask the children for pairs of factors from their times tables. They should hold up two numeral cards each time.

1. 10
2. 12
3. 18
4. 6
5. 24
6. 20
7. 16
8. 5

Ask for numbers between 0 and 10 that do not have factors apart from 1 and themselves. Write a list: 1, 2, 3, 5, 7.

83 Square roots

Resources
Number fans

Learning objective
Recall quickly multiplication facts up to 10 × 10 and use them to multiply pairs of multiples of 10 and 100; derive quickly corresponding division facts.

Type of starter
Refresh

Mental strategy
Remind children of the language and symbols of squares and square roots.

- A square number is a digit multiplied by itself eg 5 × 5. It is so called because when drawn as an array, it makes a square shape.
- The square root is the opposite, a number where the factors are a single digit eg 36 = 6 × 6.

Answers

1. 16
2. 5
3. 10
4. 9
5. 64
6. 4
7. 7
8. 81
9. 1
10. 6

Explain that you are going to call out 'square' and 'square root' questions. Children display the answer on their number fans when asked.

1. Square 4
2. Square root of 25
3. Square root of 100
4. 3^2
5. 8^2
6. Square root of 16
7. Square root of 49
8. 9^2
9. 1^2
10. Square root of 36

84 Ordering multiples

Learning objective
Recall quickly multiplication facts up to 10 × 10 and use them to multiply pairs of multiples of 10 and 100; derive quickly corresponding division facts.

Type of starter
Recall

Resources
A board or flipchart

Draw a number line 0–10 on the board:

0	1	2	3	4	5	6	7	8	9	10

Ask the questions below. If they answer correctly, individual children can write the multiple of 2 in the appropriate place under the number line (for example, 10 under 5).

1. This number is half of 20.
2. Which is the first multiple of 2?
3. This multiple of 2 is the product of 6 and 3.
4. This even number is between 6 and 10.
5. Which number is called a dozen?
6. This multiple of 2 is two more than double 7.
7. This multiple of 2 is half of 8.
8. This number is called half a dozen.
9. Double 5 plus 4.
10. Ask the children for a suitable question to give 20.

The children should chant the completed sequence together.

Answers

1. 10
2. 2
3. 18
4. 8
5. 12
6. 16
7. 4
8. 6
9. 14
10. 20

85 Finding percentages

Resources
None

Learning objective
Find fractions using division (eg $^1/_{100}$ of 5kg), and percentages of numbers and quantities (eg 10%, 5% and 15% of £80).

Type of starter
Reason

Mental strategy
Recap: 50% = $^1/_2$, 25% = $^1/_4$, 75% = $^3/_4$, 10% = $^1/_{10}$.

Answers

1.	10	9.	1.7
2.	7	10.	£2
3.	£2	11.	3
4.	£5	12.	9
5.	£9	13.	100
6.	8	14.	22
7.	30	15.	£4
8.	5		

Ask the children to raise a hand to answer these questions.

What is 50% of:

1. 20
2. 14
3. £4
4. £10
5. £18

What is 10% of:

6. 80
7. 300
8. 50
9. 17
10. £20

What is 25% of:

11. 12
12. 36
13. 400
14. 88
15. £16

86 Fraction match

Resources
A board or flipchart

Learning objective
Express a smaller whole number as a fraction of a larger one (eg recognise that 5 out of 8 is $^5/_8$); find equivalent fractions (eg $^7/_{10} = {}^{14}/_{20}$, or $^{19}/_{10} = 1\,^9/_{10}$); relate fractions to their decimal representations.

Type of starter
Refine

Mental strategy
Equivalent fractions are multiples of the numerator and denominator. Start with ½. Multiply both digits sequentially so that a pattern can be seen: $^1/_2 = {}^2/_4$; $^3/_6$; $^4/_8$; $^5/_{10}$; $^6/_{12}$, etc.

Answers

$^{10}/_{25} = {}^2/_5$, $^3/_{30} = {}^1/_{10}$,
$^6/_8 = {}^3/_4$, $^1/_2 = {}^4/_8$,
$^6/_9 = {}^2/_3$, $^1/_4 = {}^4/_{16}$,
$^2/_6 = {}^1/_3$, $^1/_5 = {}^2/_{10}$,
$^4/_{12} = {}^2/_6$

Write the following fractions on the board. Ask the children to find the equivalent pairs and join them with a line. Encourage them to explain how they worked out that they were equivalent.

$^{10}/_{25}$	$^2/_6$	¼	$^2/_{10}$	$^6/_9$	$^1/_3$	$^6/_8$	$^4/_{16}$	$^1/_5$
$^3/_{30}$	$^2/_3$	$^2/_6$	$^3/_4$	$^1/_2$	$^4/_8$	$^1/_{10}$	$^4/_{12}$	$^2/_5$

87 Numeral cards

Learning objective

Find fractions using division (eg $^1/_{100}$ of 5kg), and percentages of numbers and quantities (eg 10%, 5% and 15% of £80).

Type of starter

Recall

Mental strategy

Remind the children of previous work done:

- to find a half, we divide by 2
- when we divide a circle into quarters, we divide by 4
- if we divide a rectangle into 8 equal parts and colour 3 of them, $^3/_8$ of the shape would be coloured and $^5/_8$ would not be coloured.

Resources

A set of numeral cards 0–10 (from photocopiable page 89) for each child

Children must hold up a numeral card to show each answer.

1. How many quarters in a whole one?
2. How many quarters in two whole ones?
3. What is a quarter of 12?
4. How many fifths in a whole one?
5. What is one-fifth of 45?
6. Into how many equal parts has something been divided if the denominator of the fraction is 3?
7. What is one-third of 15?
8. What is one-quarter of 8?
9. What is three-quarters of 8?
10. If two-fifths are coloured red, how many are not coloured red?
11. What is a sixth of 42?
12. What is an eighth of 64?
13. What is half of 2?
14. How many eighths in a whole one?
15. How many halves in three whole ones?

Answers

1. 4
2. 8
3. 3
4. 5
5. 9
6. 3
7. 5
8. 2
9. 6
10. $^3/_5$
11. 7
12. 8
13. 1
14. 8
15. 6

88 Fractions Bingo

Resources
Paper and a pencil for each child

Learning objective
Express a smaller whole number as a fraction of a larger one (eg recognise that 5 out of 8 is $^5/_8$); find equivalent fractions (eg $^7/_{10} = {}^{14}/_{20}$, or $^{19}/_{10} = 1\,^9/_{10}$); relate fractions to their decimal representations.

Type of starter
Rehearse

Answers

1.	10	6.	3
2.	4	7.	9
3.	6	8.	2
4.	7	9.	5
5.	1	10.	8

The children must write five numbers between 1 and 10 (inclusive), spread out on their paper. They should cross out a number if it is the answer to a question and shout 'Bingo' when they have crossed out all five numbers.

1. How many tenths in a whole one?
2. What is half of 8?
3. How many thirds in two whole ones?
4. What is a quarter of 28?
5. What is a half of 2?
6. What is a quarter of 12?
7. What is one-tenth of 90?
8. Find one-eighth of 16.
9. What is one-sixth of 30?
10. How many quarters in two whole ones?

Percentage families

Resources
Individual whiteboards and pens for recording

Learning objective
Understand percentage as the number of parts in every 100 and express tenths and hundredths as percentages.

Type of starter
Rehearse

Mental strategy
Encourage them to understand that if they can find 50% by halving, then halving again will give them 25% and combining the two answers will give 75%.

Answers

1.	30	9.	27
2.	15	10.	£14
3.	45	11.	£7
4.	£7	12.	£21
5.	£3.50	13.	100
6.	£10.50	14.	50
7.	18	15.	150
8.	9		

Explain that you are going to ask for a percentage of an amount. The children should write the answer on their whiteboards and turn them round when you say *Show me*.

1. What is 50% of 60?
2. What is 25% of 60?
3. What is 75% of 60?
4. What is 50% of £14?
5. What is 25% of £14?
6. What is 75% of £14?
7. What is 50% of 36?
8. What is 25% of 36?
9. What is 75% of 36?
10. What is 50% of £28?
11. What is 25% of £28?
12. What is 75% of £28?
13. What is 50% of 200?
14. What is 25% of 200?
15. What is 75% of 200?

90 Doubling decimals chain

Learning objective
Use knowledge of place value and addition and subtraction of two-digit numbers to derive sums and differences and doubles and halves of decimals (eg 6.5 ± 2.7, half of 5.6, double 0.34).

Type of starter
Refine

Mental strategy
Encourage the children to double the whole number first, then the decimal, and add the two together.

Resources
None

Play 'Doubling around the room'. Ask one person to start with a given decimal number such as 1.2. The next person doubles it and it is passed on around the room until you call *change*, when the activity turns to halving. Once the original number has been reached, start another 'chain' with a different number. Suggested chains might be:

0.3, 0.6, 1.2, 2.4, 4.8, 9.6, 19.2, 38.4, 76.8

0.2, 0.4, 0.8, 1.6, 3.2, 6.4, 12.8, 25.6, 51.2, 102.4

No set answers

91 Decimals to make 10

Learning objective
Use knowledge of place value and addition and subtraction of two-digit numbers to derive sums and differences and doubles and halves of decimals (eg 6.5 ± 2.7, half of 5.6, double 0.34).

Type of starter
Rehearse

Resources
None

Divide the class into mixed-ability groups of three or four. Explain that you will ask each group in turn to say how many more are needed to make 10 (for example, 3.4 + □ = 10).

Stress that they need to listen very carefully, as their question may be linked to the previous question.

1.	6.5	6.	4.8	11.	9.6	16.	1.7
2.	7.5	7.	8.8	12.	6.1	17.	0.9
3.	8.5	8.	4.6	13.	5.1	18.	1.9
4.	2.8	9.	5.6	14.	4.1	19.	2.9
5.	3.8	10.	7.6	15.	3.7	20.	4.9

Answers

1.	3.5	11.	0.4
2.	2.5	12.	3.9
3.	1.5	13.	4.9
4.	7.2	14.	5.9
5.	6.2	15.	6.3
6.	5.2	16.	8.3
7.	1.2	17.	9.1
8.	5.4	18.	8.1
9.	4.4	19.	7.1
10.	2.4	20.	5.1

92 Totally decimal

Resources
Number fan for each child

Learning objective
Use knowledge of place value and addition and subtraction of two-digit numbers to derive sums and differences and doubles and halves of decimals (eg 6.5 ± 2.7, half of 5.6, double 0.34).

Type of starter
Refine

Mental strategy
Encourage the children to add the whole number first, then the decimal, and add the two together.

Answers

1.	8	6.	19.1
2.	9.2	7.	16.3
3.	7.2	8.	16
4.	13.4	9.	15.5
5.	13.3	10.	9.2

Use number fans to display the answers to these decimal additions:

1. 4.6 + 3.4
2. 5.3 + 3.9
3. 4.6 + 2.6
4. 7.8 + 5.6
5. 4.7 + 8.6
6. 9.4 + 9.7
7. 8.5 + 7.8
8. 9.2 + 6.8
9. 10.6 + 4.9
10. 6.5 + 2.7

93 Decimal differences

Resources
Number fan for each child

Learning objective
Use knowledge of place value and addition and subtraction of two-digit numbers to derive sums and differences and doubles and halves of decimals (eg 6.5 ± 2.7, half of 5.6, double 0.34).

Type of starter
Refine

Mental strategy
Encourage the children to count on from the decimal to the next whole number, then on in whole numbers, adding on the decimal that is left.

For example, 11.4 - 9.7: count on 0.3 from 9.7 to make 10; count on 1 to make 11; add the remaining 0.4; answer 1.7.

Answers

1.	6.3	6.	8.6
2.	4.7	7.	3.9
3.	3.7	8.	6.6
4.	6.1	9.	5.7
5.	2.4	10.	13.8

Use number fans to display the answers to these decimal subtractions.

1. 8.9 - 2.6
2. 9.2 - 4.5
3. 7.3 - 3.6
4. 13.4 - 7.3
5. 8.1 - 5.7
6. 9.4 - 0.8
7. 11.5 - 7.6
8. 8.3 - 1.7
9. 10.6 - 4.9
10. 16.5 - 2.7

Trios

Learning objective
Find fractions using division (eg $^{1}/_{100}$ of 5kg), and percentages of numbers and quantities (eg 10%, 5% and 15% of £80).

Type of starter
Rehearse

Mental strategy
Encourage the children to think in tenths or fractions that can be made into tenths which will give them the equivalent decimal. Remind them that 'percent' means 'out of 100', therefore instantly providing a fraction to be converted to tenths. The exception is ¼ and ¾ which just need to be remembered.

Resources
A board or flipchart; different coloured pens

Write the following sets of equivalents on the board, but mix them up. Ask for volunteers to choose a coloured pen and to circle an equivalent fraction, percentage and decimal, and to join the circles with a line.

10%	$^{1}/_{10}$	0.1
20%	$^{2}/_{10}$ or $^{1}/_{5}$	0.2
25%	$^{25}/_{100}$ or $^{1}/_{4}$	0.25
30%	$^{3}/_{10}$	0.3
40%	$^{4}/_{10}$	0.4
50%	$^{5}/_{10}$ or $^{1}/_{2}$	0.5
60%	$^{6}/_{10}$	0.6
70%	$^{7}/_{10}$	0.7
75%	$^{75}/_{100}$ or $^{3}/_{4}$	0.75
80%	$^{8}/_{10}$	0.8
90%	$^{9}/_{10}$	0.9
100%	$^{100}/_{100}$	1

No set answers

95 Matching on a number line

Resources
A board or flipchart

Learning objective
Express a smaller whole number as a fraction of a larger one (eg recognise that 5 out of 8 is $^5/_8$); find equivalent fractions (eg $^7/_{10}$ = $^{14}/_{20}$, or $^{19}/_{10}$ = 1 $^9/_{10}$); relate fractions to their decimal representations.

Type of starter
Refine

Answers

1. 0.5
2. 0.7
3. 0.1
4. 0.9
5. 0.4
6. 0.8
7. 0.23
8. 0.51
9. 0.44
10. 0.26

Draw two aligned number lines marked 0 to 1:

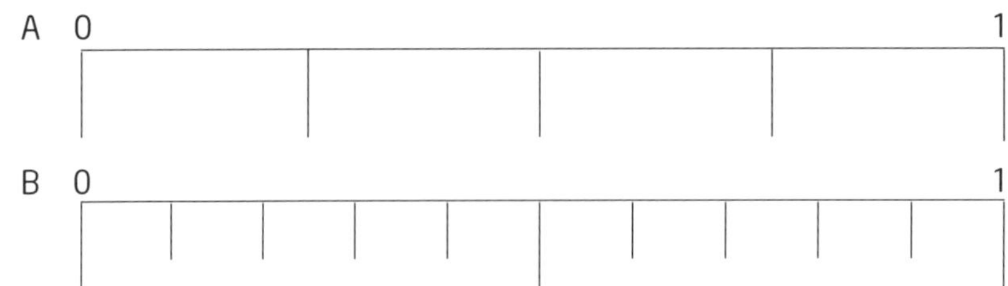

Ask volunteers to write ½, ¼ and $^2/_4$ under line A, and 0.2, 0.3, 0.5, 0.7 and 0.8 under line B. Demonstrate that ½ = 0.5. Discuss the relationships $^1/_4$ = 0.25 = $^{25}/_{100}$ and $^3/_4$ = 0.75 = $^{75}/_{100}$. Emphasise that 0.5 = $^{50}/_{100}$ = $^5/_{10}$ = $^1/_2$.

Explain that a fraction must have a denominator of 10 (or 100, 1000 and so on) before it can be written as a decimal. For example, $^1/_5$ = $^2/_{10}$ = 0.2

Ask for the decimal equivalents of:

1. $^1/_2$
2. $^7/_{10}$
3. $^1/_{10}$
4. $^9/_{10}$
5. $^2/_5$
6. $^8/_{10}$
7. $^{23}/_{100}$
8. $^{51}/_{100}$
9. $^{44}/_{100}$
10. $^{26}/_{100}$

Fractions and percentages

Learning objective
Express a smaller whole number as a fraction of a larger one (eg recognise that 5 out of 8 is $^5/_8$); find equivalent fractions (eg $^7/_{10} = {}^{14}/_{20}$, or $^{19}/_{10} = 1\ ^9/_{10}$); relate fractions to their decimal representations.

Type of starter
Refresh

Mental strategy
Remind the children that 50% means 50 parts in every hundred, so $^{50}/_{100} = ½$.

Resources
A board or flipchart; paper and a pencil for each child

No set answers

Write the following on the board, mixed up and spread out:

$\frac{1}{2}$	0.5	$\frac{50}{100}$	50%
$\frac{1}{4}$	0.25	$\frac{25}{100}$	25%
$\frac{3}{4}$	0.75	$\frac{75}{100}$	75%
$\frac{2}{5}$	0.4	$\frac{4}{10}$	40%
$\frac{3}{5}$	0.6	$\frac{6}{10}$	60%
$\frac{44}{50}$	0.88	$\frac{88}{100}$	88%

Let the children work in mixed-ability pairs for a few minutes, making 'families' of four equivalents.

Ask volunteer pairs to draw a line between a pair of equivalent terms, explaining their reasoning if possible. When all the terms are paired up, ask for volunteers to join up all four members of each family.

97 Fractions of numbers

Resources
Number fan for each child

Learning objective
Find fractions using division (eg $^1/_{100}$ of 5kg), and percentages of numbers and quantities (eg 10%, 5% and 15% of £80).

Type of starter
Rehearse

Mental strategy
Remind the children that fractions of numbers are found by using division. The denominator is the number to divide by. If the question asks for more than 1 fraction, eg $^2/_3$ or ¾, then the number should first be divided by the denominator and then the answer multiplied by the numerator.

Use number fans to display the answers to these fractions of numbers.

1. $^1/_4$ of 24
2. $^1/_2$ of 17
3. $^1/_3$ of 27
4. $^2/_3$ of 27
5. $^1/_5$ of 35
6. $^3/_5$ of 35
7. $^3/_5$ of 40
8. $^3/_4$ of 12
9. $^3/_7$ of 21
10. $^2/_9$ of 81

Answers
1. 6
2. 8.5
3. 9
4. 18
5. 7
6. 21
7. 24
8. 9
9. 9
10. 18

98 Fraction problems

Learning objective
Solve one-step and two-step problems involving whole numbers and decimals and all four operations, choosing and using appropriate calculation strategies, including calculator use.

Type of starter
Reason

Resources
Paper and pencils for each pair

The children work in pairs, using informal jottings where necessary. They should raise a hand to answer. Encourage them to explain their reasoning.

1. I have 28 pencils. Half are red and half are blue. How many are red?
2. This season we have won only a third of our nine games. How many have we won?
3. We played 12 matches last season and won $^3/_4$ of them. How many matches did we not win?
4. I have 15 counters. $^3/_5$ are green. How many of my counters are green?
5. I have 20 counters. $^7/_{10}$ are blue. How many are not blue?
6. From a box of 12 eggs, $^2/_3$ have been used. How many eggs are left?
7. I go away for a third of my six-week holiday. How many weeks am I away?
8. I have 15 sweets. $^1/_3$ are yellow, $^1/_3$ are black and $^1/_3$ are red. How many sweets are not red?
9. There are eight children at my table. $^3/_4$ are girls. How many are boys?
10. I had £2.00 and spent $^1/_4$ of it. How much did I spend?

Answers

1. 14
2. 3
3. 3
4. 9
5. 6
6. 4
7. 2
8. 10
9. 2
10. 50p

(99) Quick-fire percentages

Resources
Number fan for each child

Learning objective

Find fractions using division (eg $^1/_{100}$ of 5kg), and percentages of numbers and quantities (eg 10%, 5% and 15% of £80).

Type of starter

Rehearse

Mental strategy

Encourage the children to work on tenths (10%) and hundredths (1%). Therefore 10% of 20 is $^1/_{10}$ of 20 (20 ÷ 10 = 2). Likewise 1% is $^1/_{100}$ or 0.2.

Thereafter, all other percentages are easily found by a composite of these two percentages, for example, 11% is found by 10% +1%; 5% is easily found by halving 10%, for example, if 10% of 20 is 2, then 5% must be half of this, 1.

Also demonstrate that 99% is 100% - 1%.

Ask the children to find percentages of some amounts. They must display the answer on their number fans when you say *Show me*.

1. 10% of 30
2. 50% of 90
3. 25% of 20
4. 20% of 60
5. 5% of 120
6. 11% of 90
7. 15% of 200
8. 20% of 50
9. 99% of 200
10. 75% of 24

Answers

1. 3
2. 45
3. 5
4. 12
5. 6
6. 13.5
7. 30
8. 10
9. 198
10. 18

100 Fraction number line

Learning objective
Express a smaller whole number as a fraction of a larger one (eg recognise that 5 out of 8 is $^{5}/_{8}$); find equivalent fractions (eg $^{7}/_{10}$ = $^{14}/_{20}$, or $^{19}/_{10}$ = 1 $^{9}/_{10}$); relate fractions to their decimal representations.

Type of starter
Rehearse

Mental strategy
Ensure that the children understand how to simplify fractions to find their equivalents by dividing, for example $^{3}/_{9}$ divided by 3 gives $^{1}/_{3}$. Also discuss how $^{3}/_{3}$ equals a whole and $^{4}/_{3}$ must therefore be bigger than 1 whole.

Remind them that the bigger the denominator, the smaller the piece will be. Relate this to cake slices. For example, a cake cut into nine pieces will have smaller slices than a cake cut into three pieces.

Resources
A board or flipchart; fraction cards (enlarged from photocopiable page 95); sticky tape

Stick three of the fraction cards on the board, for example: $^{3}/_{3}$, $^{2}/_{3}$, $^{1}/_{6}$.

Discuss with the children what they know about the fractions and the decisions they would need to make to rearrange them in ascending order.

Select another fraction card from the pack and discuss where it should go in the order.

Repeat with each fraction, discussing possible equivalents and how to simplify them, shuffling and reordering as necessary.

Answers
1. $^{1}/_{9}$
2. $^{1}/_{6}$
3. $^{1}/_{5}$
4. $^{1}/_{4}$
5. $^{3}/_{9}$ (= $^{1}/_{3}$)
6. $^{2}/_{6}$ (= $^{1}/_{3}$)
7. ($^{1}/_{2}$)
8. $^{2}/_{4}$ (= $^{1}/_{2}$)
9. $^{2}/_{3}$
10. $^{3}/_{3}$ (= 1)
11. $^{4}/_{3}$ (= 1 $^{1}/_{3}$)

BLOCK E

101 The bigger share

Resources
A board or flipchart; individual whiteboards or paper and pencil for recording

Learning objective
Represent a puzzle or problem by identifying and recording the information or calculations needed to solve it; find possible solutions and confirm them in the context of the problem.

Type of starter
Reason

Mental strategy
Encourage the children to return the percentages and decimals back to tenths.

Answers

1. Jamie = $^{18}/_{20}$
   Joe $^{17}/_{20}$
   Lee = $^{16}/_{20}$
2. 0.2 = $^{1}/_{5}$ = 20%
3. 'Sloppy Kit' = 80%
   'Munchiows' = 75%

Write the following scenarios on the board. Ask the children to discuss, in pairs, which is the greater and smaller amount and to be prepared to explain their ideas to the rest of the class.

1. Three friends were discussing their spelling test results. They all did the same test. Lee said that he had beaten his friends because he had scored 80%. Joe disagreed because he scored $^{17}/_{20}$, his best score this term. Jamie thought they were both wrong because he had scored 0.9 of the total available in the test. Who scored the highest/lowest?
2. Gran was cutting a chocolate cake for tea. She offered Alice 0.2 of the cake, Kadheja $^{1}/_{5}$ and Mo 20%. Who had the biggest slice of cake?
3. $^{8}/_{10}$ cats were said by their owners to prefer 'Sloppy Kit' cat food. In another survey, 75% of cat owners said their favourite cat food was 'Munchiows'. Which was the most popular cat food?

(102) What's for tea?

Learning objective
Use sequences to scale numbers up or down; solve problems involving proportions of quantities (eg decrease quantities in a recipe designed to feed six people).

Type of starter
Reason

Resources
A board or flipchart; individual whiteboards or paper and pencils for recording

Write the following recipe on the board:

Tomato and cheese tart (serves 4)

250g puff pastry
50g tomato puree
1 teaspoon oregano
120g grated cheese
2 tomatoes
12 olives
75g mushrooms

Ask the children to rewrite the recipe to feed:

1. 2 people,
2. 12 people
3. 6 people.

They must be prepared to explain how they did it.

Answers

1. **Tomato and cheese tart (serves 2) (÷ 2)**
125g puff pastry
25g tomato puree
½ teaspoon oregano
60g grated cheese
1 tomato
6 olives
37.5g mushrooms

2. **Tomato and cheese tart (serves 12) (× 3)**
750g puff pastry
150g tomato puree
3 teaspoons oregano
360g grated cheese
6 tomatoes
36 olives
225g mushrooms

3. **Tomato and cheese tart (serves 6) (× 1½)**
375g puff pastry
75g tomato puree
1½ teaspoons oregano
180g grated cheese
3 tomatoes
18 olives
112.5g mushrooms

Place value arrow cards

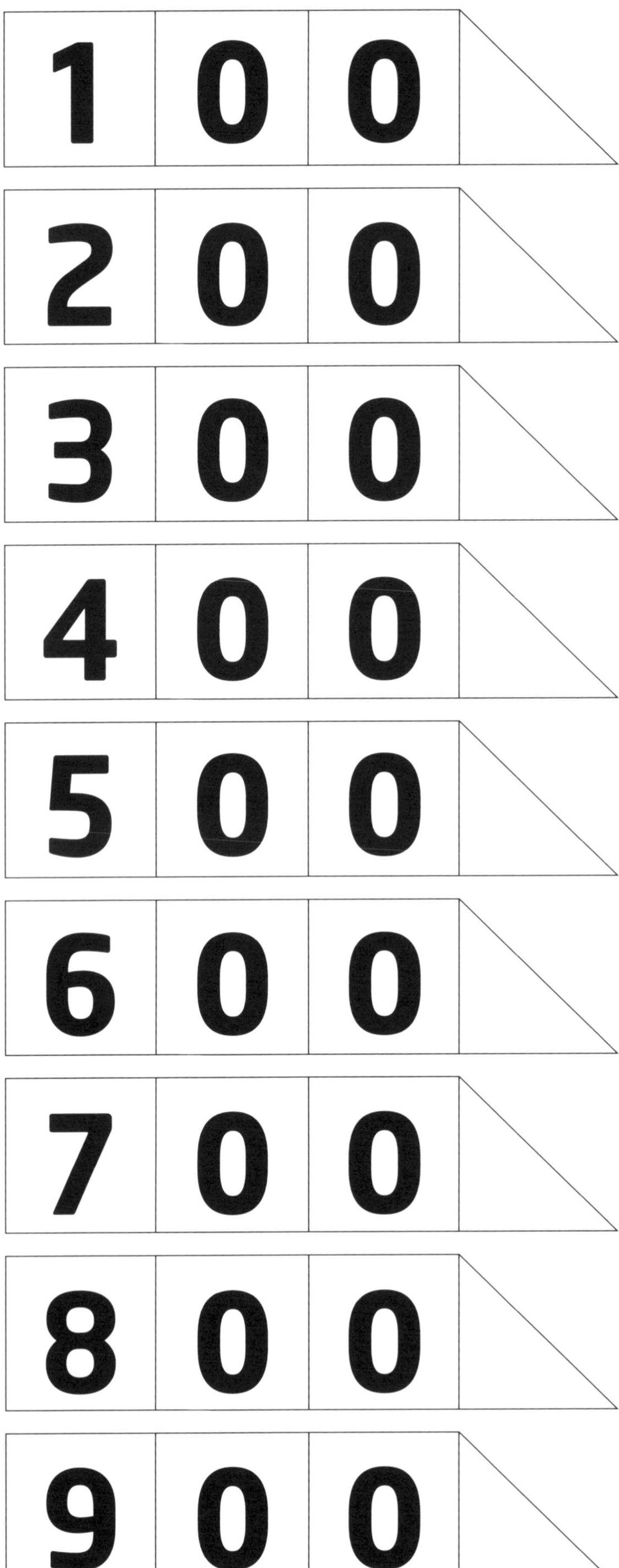

Place value arrow cards

1	0
2	0
3	0
4	0
5	0
6	0
7	0
8	0
9	0

Place value arrow cards

Numeral cards 0-10

0	1	2
3	4	5
6	7	8
9	10	

Snap cards set 1

12	14	16	18
21	24	27	28
32	36	20	25
30	35	40	45

Snap cards set 2

18	24	30	36
42	48	54	28
35	49	56	63
32	40	64	72
21	27	45	81

Shape cards

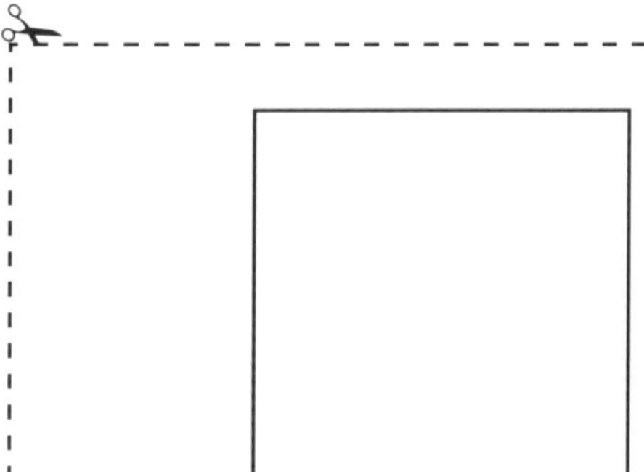

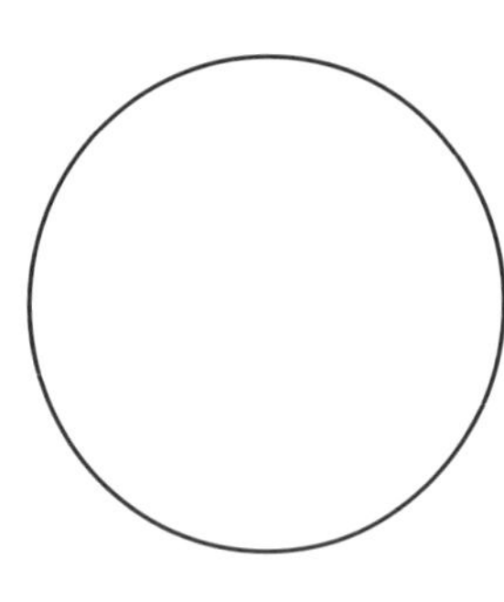

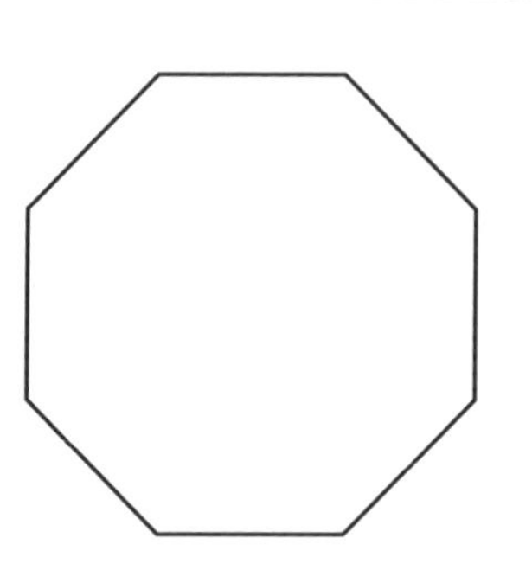

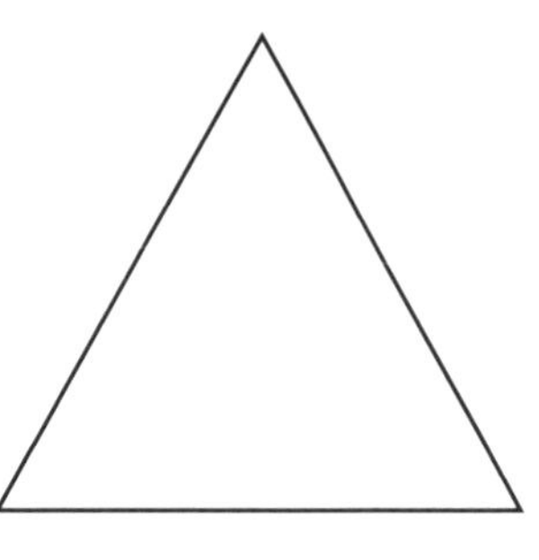

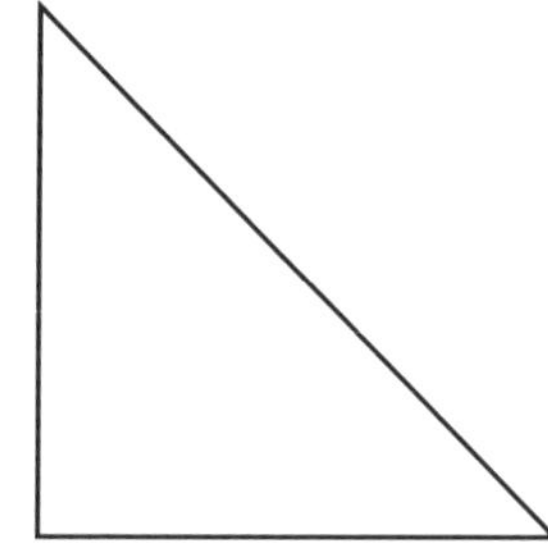

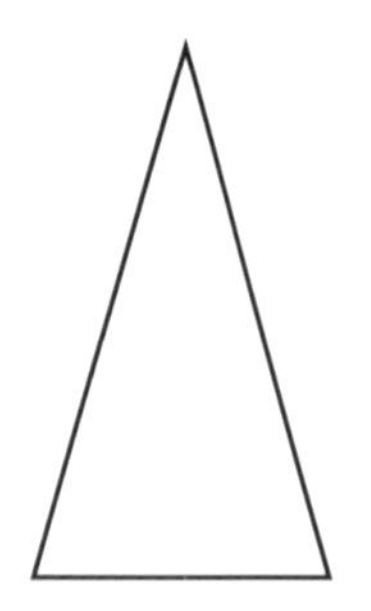

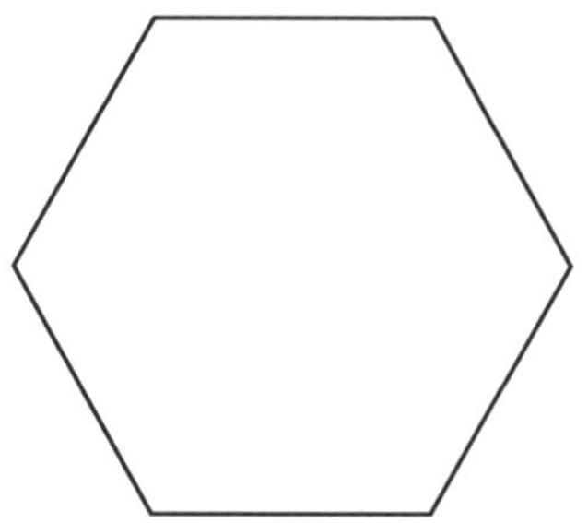

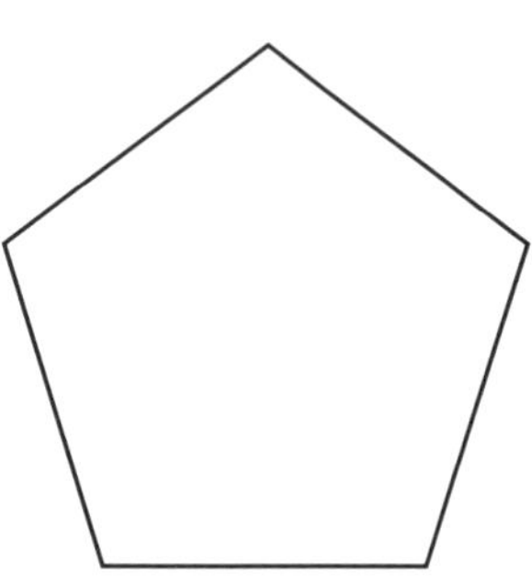

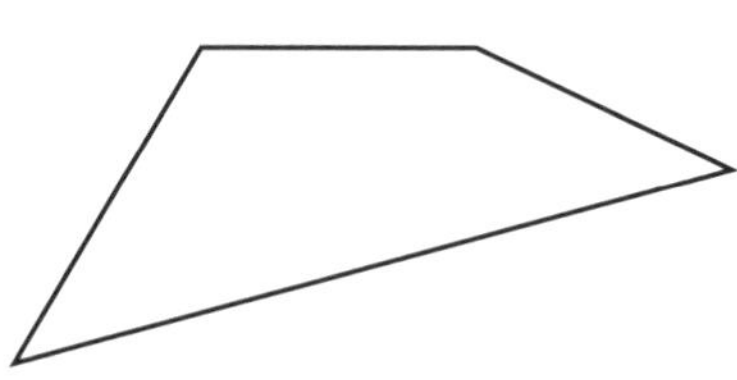

'Follow me' cards

(12) 3 × 7	(21) 4 × 6	(24) 32 ÷ 4	(8) 35 ÷ 5
(7) 9 × 3	(27) 2 × 8	(16) 30 ÷ 6	(5) 28 ÷ 7
(4) 4 × 9	(36) 7 × 6	(42) 10 × 7	(70) 60 ÷ 10
(6) 18 ÷ 9	(2) 7 × 7	(49) 3 × 6	(18) 40 ÷ 2
(20) 44 ÷ 4	(11) 9 × 6	(54) 8 × 8	(64) 38 halve it
(19) 24 ÷ 8	(3) 48 double it	(96) 72 ÷ 8	(9) 8 × 7
(56) 5 × 5	(25) 17 double it	(34) 5 × 8	(40) 9 × 7
(63) 52 halve it	(26) 10 ÷ 10	(1) 2 × 5	(10) 3 × 4

Types of graph

A

Bar graph

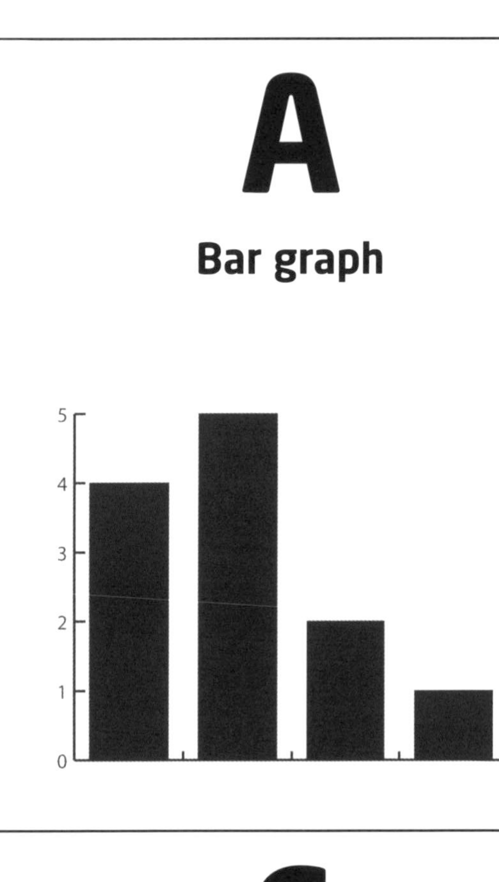

B

Line graph

C

Bar line graph

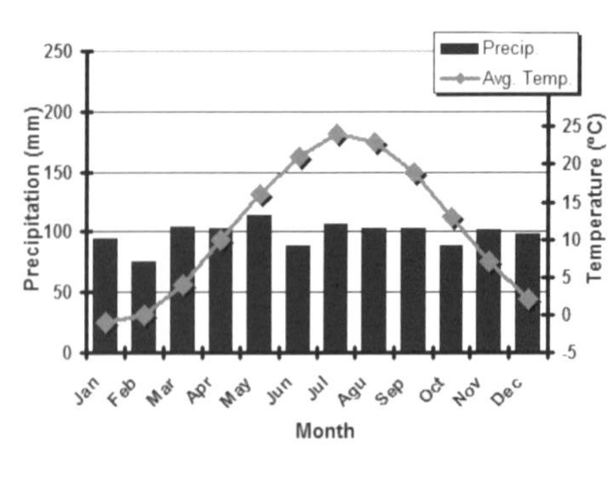

D

Pictogram

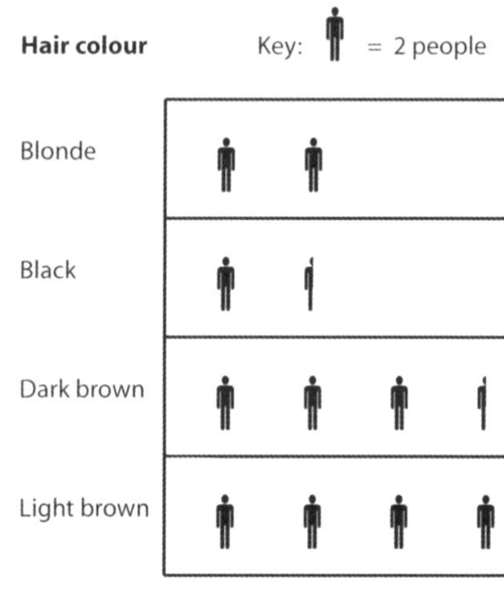

Fraction cards

$\frac{3}{3}$	$\frac{2}{3}$
$\frac{3}{9}$	$\frac{4}{3}$
$\frac{2}{6}$	$\frac{1}{5}$
$\frac{1}{4}$	$\frac{2}{4}$
$\frac{1}{9}$	$\frac{1}{6}$
$\frac{1}{2}$	

Level 4: Oral and mental assessments

Teachers' notes

Time: 20 minutes for each complete paper.

- Children should sit so that they cannot see each other's work.
- Do not explain questions or read numbers to the children.
- The test may be administered to groups of children or to the whole class.
- There are 20 marks available for each paper.

Delivering the tests

- Read each question to the children twice.
- Allow five seconds each for questions 1-5, ten seconds for questions 6-15 and fifteen seconds for questions 16-20.
- Answers to be recorded on the answer sheets provided.

Say to the children:

'I am going to read some questions for you to answer. I will read each question twice. You will have five seconds to answer the first five questions, then ten seconds to answer the next ten questions and finally 15 seconds for the last five questions.'

'For most of the questions you will write your answer in a box.' [Show example.]

'For some questions you may need to tick the right answer.'

'If you make a mistake, you should cross it out and write your answer again clearly.'

Levelling the children

Add up the marks.

(Possible total: 20 marks)

Below Level 4	0 - 7 marks
Low Level 4	8 - 12 marks
Secure Level 4	13 - 15 marks
High Level 4	16 - 20 marks

This assessment reflects a child's performance in mental maths. When awarding an end-of-year teacher assessment level, teachers also need to consider a child's performance on periodic and day-to-day assessments over all learning objectives.

Test 1: Mental maths assessment

Oral and mental questions (page 1 of 2)

Time: 20 minutes

- Read each question twice to the children.
- Answers to be recorded on the answer sheet on pages 99-101.
- One mark per question: 20 marks total.
- Allow five seconds for each answer for questions 1-5, ten seconds for questions 6-15, and fifteen seconds for questions 16-20.

	Question	Answer
1	What is 8 × 7?	56
2	Calculate 65 × 100.	6500
3	Fifty-four hundreds is the same as which number?	5400
4	How many do I add to three-fifths to make one whole 1?	$^2/_5$
5	How many metres is 2460 centimetres?	24.6 metres
6	How many right angles are there in 360 degrees?	4
7	A regular hexagon has a perimeter of 42 centimetres. How long is each side?	7cm
8	Add 2.4 to 3.7.	6.1
9	*(Look at the numbers.)* I add a number to 325 to make 1000. Tick the correct number.	675
10	What is 5% of £3000?	£150

Test 1: Mental maths assessment

Oral and mental questions (page 2 of 2)

	Question	Answer
11	Write a prime number that is more than 50 but less 60.	53 or 59
12	25% of days in October will be windy. Tick the most appropriate statement.	uncertain
13	*(Look at the Venn diagram.)* Tick the number that is in the wrong position.	48
14	When I divide a number by 6 the answer is 40. What was my number?	240
15	*(Look at the fractions.)* Tick the fraction that is the same as a quarter.	$^{3}/_{12}$
16	The area of a rectangle is 640 square centimetres. The length of one side is 20 centimetres. What is the breadth?	32cm
17	I am thinking of a number. I halve it and then add 20 to my total. My answer is 48. What was my number?	56
18	Six apples weigh 1.8 kilograms. How much would one apple weigh?	300g
19	Subtract two hundred from seven hundred and eighty-four.	584
20	I am facing south-west and turn clockwise through two right angles. What direction am I now facing?	north-east

End of test

Name Date

Test 1: Mental maths assessment

Oral and mental assessment answer sheet (1 of 3)

Time: 5 seconds per question

	Answer	Mark
1		
2		
3		
4		
5		

Time: 10 seconds per question

	Answer				Mark
6					
7					
8					
9	775	625	675	725	
10					

Name Date

Test 1: Mental maths assessment

Oral and mental assessment answer sheet (2 of 3)

Time: 10 seconds per question

	Answer				Mark
11					
12	fair ☐	uncertain ☐	certain ☐		
13	multiples of 8: 40, 56, 16; both: 24; multiples of 3: 15, 33, 48				
14					
15	$\frac{3}{5}$	$\frac{3}{12}$	$\frac{5}{8}$	$\frac{2}{6}$	

Name Date

Test 1: Mental maths assessment

Oral and mental assessment answer sheet (3 of 3)

Time: 15 seconds per question

	Answer	Mark
16		
17		
18		
19		
20		
End of test	**Total**	

Test 2: Mental maths assessment

Oral and mental questions (page 1 of 2)

Time: 20 minutes

- Read each question twice to the children.
- Answers to be recorded on the answer sheet on pages 104-105.
- 1 mark per question: 20 marks total.
- Allow five seconds for each answer for questions 1-5, ten seconds for questions 6-15, and fifteen seconds for questions 16-20.

	Question	Answer
1	What is 81 ÷ 9?	9
2	Calculate 6.2 × 10.	62
3	5000 + 400 + 67 =	5467
4	0.3 equals what fraction?	$^{3}/_{10}$
5	2.5 litres equals how many millilitres?	2500ml
6	I am thinking of a triangle. It has two equal angles. What is the name of this triangle?	isosceles
7	What is the square root of 64?	8
8	A book has a selling price of £2, but has been reduced by 25%. How much is it now?	£1.50
9	*(Look at the shapes.)* Tick the rhombus.	✔
10	I start a journey at 6.20 and finish it at 7:05. How long was my journey?	45 minutes

Test 2: Mental maths assessment

Oral and mental questions (page 2 of 2)

<table>
<tr><th></th><th>Question</th><th>Answer</th></tr>
<tr><td>11</td><td>Fill in the blank spaces to complete the table.</td><td>
<table>
<tr><th>3D shape</th><th>vertices</th><th>edges</th><th>faces</th></tr>
<tr><td>cube</td><td>8</td><td>12</td><td>6</td></tr>
<tr><td>square-based pyramid</td><td>5</td><td>8</td><td>5</td></tr>
<tr><td>cone</td><td>1</td><td>1</td><td>2</td></tr>
</table>
</td></tr>
<tr><td>12</td><td>(Look at the jug.) This jug holds 500 millilitres. I pour out 50 millilitres. How much is left?</td><td>325ml</td></tr>
<tr><td>13</td><td>(Look at the numbers.) Tick the smallest number.</td><td>4.26</td></tr>
<tr><td>14</td><td>I have 60 marbles. Two-fifths are blue and the rest are red. How many are red?</td><td>36</td></tr>
<tr><td>15</td><td>(Look at the angles.) Tick the angle that is about 45°.</td><td>✔</td></tr>
<tr><td>16</td><td>(Look at the pictogram.) The pictogram shows how much money Jack spends each week. He earns £150. How much will he have left?</td><td>£90</td></tr>
<tr><td>17</td><td>Six bags of crisps weigh 54g. What would be the mass of 20 bags?</td><td>180g</td></tr>
<tr><td>18</td><td>Add together 340 and 90 and then subtract 35.</td><td>395</td></tr>
<tr><td>19</td><td>Subtract 0.4 from 2.3.</td><td>1.9</td></tr>
<tr><td>20</td><td>The temperature inside a plane is 25° but outside it is -32°. What is the difference in temperature?</td><td>57°</td></tr>
</table>

End of test

Name Date

Test 2: Mental maths assessment

Oral and mental assessment answer sheet (1 of 2)

Time: 5 seconds per question

	Answer	Mark
1		
2		
3		
4		
5		

Time: 10 seconds per question

	Answer	Mark
6		
7		
8		
9	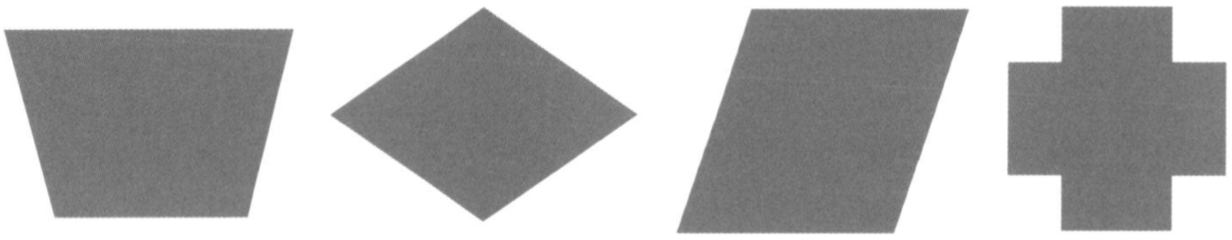	
10		
11	(see table below)	

3D shape	vertices	edges	faces
cube	8		6
square-based pyramid	5	8	
cone		1	2

Name Date

Test 2: Mental maths assessment

Oral and mental assessment answer sheet (2 of 2)

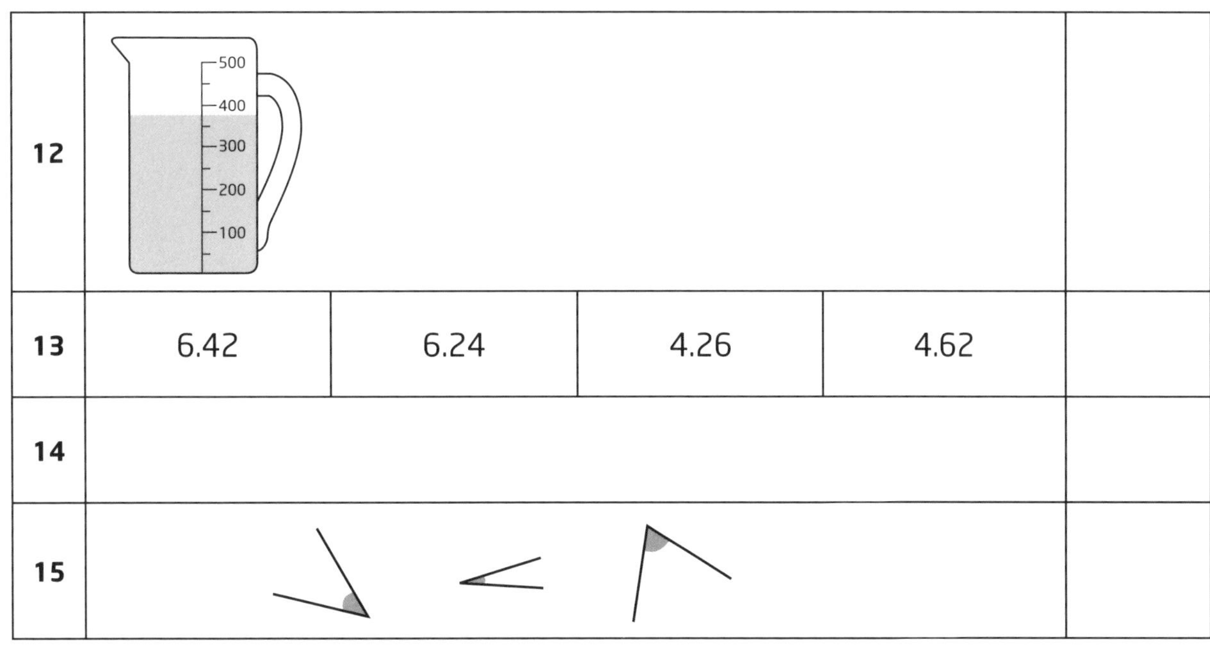

12					
13	6.42	6.24	4.26	4.62	
14					
15					

Time: 15 seconds per question

	Answer	Mark
16	clothes £5 food £5 £5 £5 petrol £5 £5 £5 £5 gas £5 £5 telephone £5 £5	
17		
18		
19		
20		

End of test	**Total**	

Level 5: Oral and mental assessments

Teachers' notes

Time: 20 minutes for each complete paper.

- Children should sit so that they cannot see each other's work.
- Do not explain questions or read numbers to the children.
- The test may be administered to groups of children or to the whole class.
- There are 20 marks available for each paper.

Delivering the tests

- Read each question to the children twice.
- Allow five seconds each for questions 1-5, ten seconds for questions 6-15 and fifteen seconds for questions 16-20.
- Answers to be recorded on the answer sheets provided.

Say to the children:

'I am going to read some questions for you to answer. I will read each question twice. You will have five seconds to answer the first five questions, then ten seconds to answer the next ten questions and finally 15 seconds for the last five questions.'

'For most of the questions you will write your answer in a box.' [Show example.]

'For some questions you may need to tick the right answer.'

'If you make a mistake, you should cross it out and write your answer again clearly.'

Levelling the children

Add up the marks.

(Possible total: 20 marks)

Below Level 5	0 - 7 marks
Low Level 5	8 - 12 marks
Secure Level 5	13 - 15 marks
High Level 5	16 - 20 marks

This assessment reflects a child's performance in mental maths. When awarding an end-of-year teacher assessment level, teachers also need to consider a child's performance on periodic and day-to-day assessments over all learning objectives.

Test 1: Mental maths assessment

Oral and mental questions (page 1 of 2)

Time: 20 minutes

- Read each question twice to the children.
- Answers to be recorded on the answer sheet on pages 109-110.
- One mark per question: 20 marks total.
- Allow five seconds for each answer for questions 1-5, ten seconds for questions 6-15, and fifteen seconds for questions 16-20.

	Question	Answer
1	What is 0.7 as a percentage?	70%
2	Calculate 6.3 ÷ 100.	0.063
3	What is the square root of 81?	9
4	How many do I add to 457 to make 1000?	543
5	What is the product of 40 and 60?	2400
6	A right-angled triangle has a second angle of 30°. How much does the third angle measure?	60°
7	*(Look at the number sequence.)* What is the next number in this sequence? Write it in the empty box.	3(.0)
8	*(Look at the decimals.)* Tick the decimal that is equal to two-fifths.	0.4
9	How many 20p coins are there in £3.40?	17
10	Write two factors of 56 that have a difference of 10.	14, 4

Test 1: Mental maths assessment

Oral and mental questions (page 2 of 2)

	Question	Answer
11	I use two eggs to make 12 buns. How many eggs will I use to make 54 buns?	9
12	How many eights are there in 720?	90
13	Add 6.4 to 4.7.	11.1
14	The radius of a rug is 525 centimetres. What is its diameter?	1050cm or 10.5m
15	Imagine a pentagonal-based pyramid. How many faces does it have?	6
16	I leave Manchester at 10:20am and arrive in Dallas 14 hours later. Dallas is 6 hours behind GMT. What time is it in Dallas when I arrive?	18:20 or 6:20pm
17	Garden furniture was on sale for £620.00. It has been reduced by 20%. How much is it now?	£496
18	Katie is 63 centimetres tall. Daniel is one-third taller than that. How tall is Daniel?	84cm
19	*(Look at the fractions.)* Tick the smallest fraction.	$^{3}/_{19}$
20	*(Look at the number line.)* The difference between A and B is 280. What are the values of A and B?	A = -120 B = 160

End of test

Name Date

Test 1: Mental maths assessment

Oral and mental assessment answer sheet (1 of 2)

Time: 5 seconds per question

	Answer	Mark
1		
2		
3		
4		
5		

Time: 10 seconds per question

	Answer					Mark
6						
7	4.2	3.8	3.4			
8	0.2	0.3	0.4	0.5	0.6	
9						
10						

Name Date

Test 1: Mental maths assessment

Oral and mental assessment answer sheet (2 of 2)

Time: 10 seconds per question

	Answer	Mark
11		
12		
13		
14		
15		

Time: 15 seconds per question

	Answer				Mark
16					
17					
18					
19	$\frac{2}{5}$	$\frac{17}{18}$	$\frac{3}{19}$	$\frac{11}{17}$	
20	**A**	**0**		**B**	
	A =		B =		
End of test			**Total**		

Mental maths teacher record sheet

Teacher's name: ____________________

Name of starter	PNS objectives covered	Block/unit	Date activity was used